PEARSON
TEXAS
GEOMETRY

INTERACTIVE MATH JOURNAL
STUDENT COMPANION

PEARSON

Boston, Massachusetts • Chandler, Arizona • Glenview, Illinois • Hoboken, New Jersey

ISBN-13: 978-0-13-330069-7
ISBN-10:   0-13-330069-2

PEARSON

6   17

 Contents

▶▶▶ 3-Act Math T1

Topic 1   The Mystery Spokes T1

Topic 2   Bad Advice Guy T3

Topic 3   Parallel Paving Company T5

Topic 4   Check It Out! T7

Topic 5   Making It Fair T9

Topic 6   The Mystery Sides T11

Topic 7   You Be the Judge T13

Topic 8   The Perplexing Polygon T15

Topic 9   Make It Right.............T17

Topic 10 The Impossible Measurement T19

Topic 11 Round We Go T21

Topic 12 Earth Watch.............T23

Topic 13 The Great Enlargement T25

Topic 14 Box 'Em Up T27

Topic 15 Place Your Guess T29

UNIT 1 **LOGICAL ARGUMENT AND CONSTRUCTIONS: PROOF AND CONGRUENCE**

Topic 1   Tools of Geometry................................... 1

Topic 2   Reasoning and Proof................................ 31

Topic 3   Parallel and Perpendicular Lines..................... 67

Topic 4   Congruent Triangles 123

Topic 5   Relationships Within Triangles 165

Topic 6   Polygons and Quadrilaterals........................ 213

UNIT 2 **COORDINATE AND TRANSFORMATIONAL GEOMETRY**

Topic 7   Coordinate Geometry.............................. 251

Topic 8   Transformational Geometry......................... 269

UNIT 3 **SIMILARITY, PROOF, AND TRIGONOMETRY**

Topic 9   Similarity... 317

Topic 10 Right Triangles and Trigonometry 347

UNIT 4 **CIRCLES**

Topic 11 Circle Measurement................................ 373

Topic 12 Theorems about Circles............................. 397

UNIT 5 **TWO-DIMENSIONAL AND THREE-DIMENSIONAL FIGURES**

Topic 13 Area 421

Topic 14 Surface Area and Volume 453

UNIT 6 **PROBABILITY**

Topic 15 Probability 499

Using Your **Interactive Math Journal: Student Companion** with Success

The **Interactive Math Journal: Student Companion** is your in-class write-in worktext for *Pearson Texas Geometry*. You will use your write-in worktext to work out solutions to problems presented and to check your understanding of concepts learned. Your **Interactive Math Journal: Student Companion** is available in print or as an ACTIVe-book, accessible through **PeasonTEXAS.com**.

STEP ONE

INTERACTIVE LEARNING

As your teacher projects the **Solve It** activity, you can collaborate with classmates to determine a solution to the problem posed. Work out your solution in your **Interactive Math Journal: Student Companion**. You can also take notes about the concepts presented. After a discussion of the solution, you'll be asked to complete the reflection question and think about the processes and strategies you used to solve the problem.

Look for the BouncePages icon on some **Solve Its**. Scan the page to access an animation for the problem.

Interactive Exploration

Vocabulary Online

STEP TWO

GUIDED PROBLEM SOLVING

During the **Guided Problem Solving** part of the lesson, your teacher will guide you through the problems that introduce or reinforce important concepts and skills. After each problem, you work on the **Got It**, an exercise that applies the concepts and skills from the problem, to help solidify your understanding of these concepts.

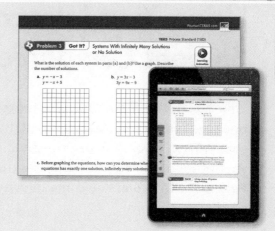

Learning Animation

STEP THREE

LESSON CHECK

At the end of each lesson is the **Lesson Check**. Each Lesson Check has two parts:

- **Do You Know How?** exercises help you gauge your procedural fluency.
- **Do You Understand?** exercises can give you a sense of how well you understand the lesson concepts.

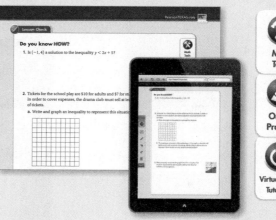

Math Tools

Online Practice

Virtual Nerd Tutorials

TEXAS Test Practice

Your **Interactive Math Journal: Student Companion** also includes **Texas Test Practice**. For each lesson, you'll find a page of practice exercises. Your teacher may assign these practice items to complete in class or for homework.

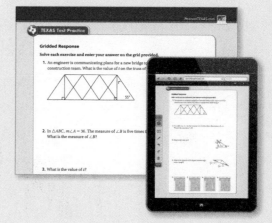

Using Your **Interactive Math Journal: Student Companion** ACTIVe-book

Your **Interactive Math Journal: Student Companion** is available as an ACTIVe-book, an interactive electronic workbook, that you can access on any device. In your ACTIVe-book, you can complete all of the exercises, and you can record all of your notes or reminders and access them any time and anywhere you can log in to **PearsonTEXAS.com**. You can also use the built-in communication tool to ask your teachers questions.

At the lesson level, you can access not just the pages in your **Interactive Math Journal: Student Companion**, but the digital assets as well. With the click of a tile, you can revisit the **Solve It** or any of the lesson problems.

Click on the tiles along the top row to work through the lesson.

Use the different tools in the toolbar to record your answers and notes.
Don't forget to click SAVE when you have finished.

Notice the ACTIVe-book toolbar on the left. You can place the toolbar where it is most convenient.

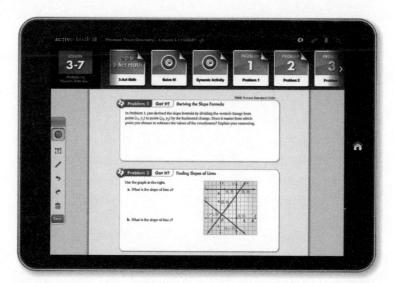

These features can help you stay organized and manage your work. You can see your assignments, chat with your teacher, bookmark a page, or access digital support tools.

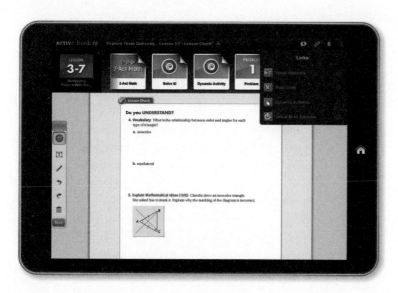

You have quick access to Math Tools, Visual Glossary, or even Online Homework.

3-Act Math

The Mystery Spokes

Interactive
Exploration

1. What is the first question that comes to mind after watching the video?

2. Write down the main question you will answer about what you saw in the video.

3. Make an initial conjecture that answers this main question.

4. Explain how you arrived at your conjecture.

5. Write a number that you know is too small for each object.

6. Write a number that you know is too large for each object.

7. What information will be useful to know to answer the main question? How can you get it? How will you use that information?

8. Use the math that you have learned in this topic to refine your conjecture.

9. Is your refined conjecture for each object between the highs and lows you set up earlier?

10. Did your refined conjecture match each actual answer exactly? If not, what might explain the difference?

3-Act Math

Bad Advice Guy

Interactive Exploration

1. Write down the main question you will answer about what you saw in the video.

2. Make initial conjectures about each of Bad Advice Guy's statements. Which seem right and wrong?

3. What information will be useful to know to answer the main question? How can you get it? How will you use that information?

4. Use the tools you have learned in this topic to refine the conjectures you made earlier.

3-Act Math

Parallel Paving Company

Interactive Exploration

1. What is the first question that comes to mind after watching the video?

2. Write down the main question you will answer about what you saw in the video.

3. Make an initial conjecture that answers this main question.

4. Explain how you arrived at your conjecture.

5. What information will be useful to know to answer the main question? How can you get it? How will you use that information?

6. Use the math that you have learned in this topic to refine your conjecture.

7. Did your refined conjecture match the actual answer exactly? If not, what might explain the difference?

3-Act Math

Check It Out!

Interactive
Exploration

1. What is the first question that comes to mind after watching the video?

2. Write down the main question you will answer about what you saw in the video.

3. Make an initial conjecture that answers this main question.

4. Explain how you arrived at your conjecture.

5. What information will be useful to know to answer the main question? How can you get it? How will you use that information?

6. Use the math that you have learned in this topic to refine your conjecture.

3-Act Math

Making It Fair

Interactive
Exploration

1. What is the first question that comes to mind after watching the video?

2. Write down the main question you will answer about what you saw in the video.

3. Make an initial conjecture that answers this main question.

4. Explain how you arrived at your conjecture.

5. What information will be useful to know to answer the main question? How can you get it? How will you use that information?

6. Use the math that you have learned in this topic to refine your conjecture.

7. Did your refined conjecture match the actual answer exactly? If not, what might explain the difference?

3-Act Math

The Mystery Sides

Interactive Exploration

1. What is the first question that comes to mind after watching the video?

2. Write down the main question you will answer about what you saw in the video.

3. Make an initial conjecture that answers this main question.

4. Explain how you arrived at your conjecture.

5. Write a number that you know is too small for each object.

6. Write a number that you know is too large for each object.

7. What information will be useful to know to answer the main question? How can you get it? How will you use that information?

8. Use the math that you have learned in this topic to refine your conjecture.

9. Is your refined conjecture for each object between the highs and lows you set up earlier?

10. Did your refined conjecture match each actual answer exactly? If not, what might explain the difference?

3-Act Math

You Be the Judge

Interactive
Exploration

1. What is the first question that comes to mind after watching the video?

2. Write down the main question you will answer about what you saw in the video.

3. Make an initial conjecture that answers this main question.

4. Explain how you arrived at your conjecture.

5. What information will be useful to know to answer the main question? How can you get it? How will you use that information?

6. Use the math that you have learned in this topic to refine your conjecture.

7. Did your refined conjecture match the actual answer exactly? If not, what might explain the difference?

The Perplexing Polygon

Interactive Exploration

1. What is the first question that comes to mind after watching the video?

2. Write down the main question you will answer about what you saw in the video.

3. Make an initial conjecture that answers this main question.

4. Explain how you arrived at your conjecture.

5. What information will be useful to know to answer the main question? How can you get it? How will you use that information?

6. Use the math that you have learned in this topic to refine your conjecture.

7. Did your refined conjecture match the actual answer exactly? If not, what might explain the difference?

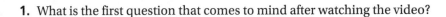

3-Act Math

Make It Right

Interactive Exploration

1. What is the first question that comes to mind after watching the video?

2. Write down the main question you will answer about what you saw in the video.

3. Make an initial conjecture that answers this main question.

4. Draw and label a figure to illustrate how you arrived at your conjecture.

5. Write a number that you know is too small.

6. Write a number that you know is too large.

7. What information will be useful to know to answer the main question? How can you get it? How will you use that information?

8. Use the math that you have learned in this topic to refine your conjecture.

9. Is your refined conjecture between the highs and lows you set up earlier?

10. Did your refined conjecture match the actual answer exactly? If not, what might explain the difference?

3-Act Math

The Impossible Measurement

Interactive
Exploration

1. What is the first question that comes to mind after watching the video?

2. Write down the main question you will answer about what you saw in the video.

3. Make an initial conjecture that answers this main question.

4. Explain how you arrived at your conjecture.

5. Write a number that you know is too small.

6. Write a number that you know is too large.

7. What information will be useful to know to answer the main question? How can you get it? How will you use that information?

8. Use the math that you have learned in this topic to refine your conjecture.

9. Is your refined conjecture between the highs and lows you set up earlier?

10. Did your refined conjecture match the actual answer exactly? If not, what might explain the difference?

Topic 10 | 3-Act Math

T20

3-Act Math

Round We Go

Interactive Exploration

1. What is the first question that comes to mind after watching the video?

2. Write down the main question you will answer about what you saw in the video.

3. Make an initial conjecture that answers this main question.

4. Explain how you arrived at your conjecture.

5. Write a number that you know is too small.

6. Write a number that you know is too large.

7. What information will be useful to know to answer the main question? How can you get it? How will you use that information?

8. Use the math that you have learned in this topic to refine your conjecture.

9. Is your refined conjecture between the highs and lows you set up earlier?

10. Did your refined conjecture match the actual answer exactly? If not, what might explain the difference?

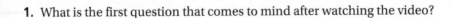

Earth Watch

Interactive Exploration

1. What is the first question that comes to mind after watching the video?

2. Write down the main question you will answer about what you saw in the video.

3. Make an initial conjecture that answers this main question.

4. Explain how you arrived at your conjecture.

5. Write a number that you know is too small.

6. Write a number that you know is too large.

7. What information will be useful to know to answer the main question? How can you get it? How will you use that information?

8. Use the math that you have learned in this topic to refine your conjecture.

9. Is your refined conjecture between the highs and lows you set up earlier?

10. Did your refined conjecture match the actual answer exactly? If not, what might explain the difference?

3-Act Math

The Great Enlargement

1. What is the first question that comes to mind after watching the video?

2. Write down the main question you will answer about what you saw in the video.

3. Make an initial conjecture that answers this main question.

4. Explain how you arrived at your conjecture.

5. Write a number that you know is too small.

6. Write a number that you know is too large.

7. What information will be useful to know to answer the main question? How can you get it? How will you use that information?

8. Use the math that you have learned in this topic to refine your conjecture.

9. Is your refined conjecture between the highs and lows you set up earlier?

10. Did your refined conjecture match the actual answer exactly? If not, what might explain the difference?

Box 'Em Up

Interactive Exploration

1. What is the first question that comes to mind after watching the video?

2. Write down the main question you will answer about what you saw in the video.

3. Make an initial conjecture that answers this main question.

4. Explain how you arrived at your conjecture.

5. What information will be useful to know to answer the main question? How can you get it? How will you use that information?

6. Use the math that you have learned in this topic to refine your conjecture.

7. Did your refined conjecture match the actual answer exactly? If not, what might explain the difference?

3-Act Math

Place Your Guess

Interactive
Exploration

1. What is the first question that comes to mind after watching the video?

2. Write down the main question you will answer about what you saw in the video.

3. Make an initial conjecture that answers this main question.

4. Explain how you arrived at your conjecture.

5. What information will be useful to know to answer the main question? How can you get it? How will you use that information?

6. Use the math that you have learned in this topic to refine your conjecture.

7. Did your refined conjecture match the actual answer exactly? If not, what might explain the difference?

2-1 Patterns and Conjectures

PearsonTEXAS.com

 **SOLVE IT!**

Scan page for an interactive
version of this Solve It.

Suppose you fold a piece of paper in half. When you unfold it, the paper is divided into rectangles. As you increase the number of folds, you increase the number of rectangles. How many rectangles would you get if you folded a piece of paper in half eight times? Explain.

Interactive
Exploration

Vocabulary
Online

Three folds

Select Techniques to Solve Problems (1)(C) What other techniques could you use to solve the problem? Select one and explain how you would use it.

Lesson 2-1 | Patterns and Conjectures

31

Problem 1 | Got It? | Finding and Using a Pattern

Learning
Animation

What are the next two terms in each sequence?

a. 45, 40, 35, 30, . . .

b.

 Describe the pattern you found in each sequence. Then use your own ideas to write a numerical or geometric sequence. Trade with your partner and find the next two terms in each other's sequence.

TEKS Process Standard (1)(D)

Problem 2 | Got It? | Making a Conjecture

Learning
Animation

What conjecture can you make about the 21st term in R, W, B, R, W, B, . . . ?

Problem 3 | Got It? | Collecting Information to Make a Conjecture

Learning
Animation

What conjecture can you make about the sum of the first 30 odd numbers?

TEKS Process Standard (1)(A)

Problem 4 **Got It?** Making a Prediction

Learning
Animation

a. In Problem 5, you made a conjecture about the number of backpacks the company will sell in May. What conjecture can you make about backpack sales in June?

Backpacks Sold

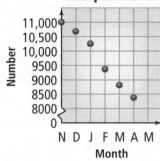

b. Is it reasonable to use this graph to make a conjecture about sales in August? Explain.

Problem 5 **Got It?** Verifying a Conjecture Is False Using a Counterexample

Learning
Animation

What is a counterexample for each conjecture?

a. If a flower is red, it is a rose.

b. One and only one plane exists through any three points.

c. When you multiply a number by 3, the product is divisible by 6.

Lesson 2-1 | Patterns and Conjectures

Lesson Check

Do you know HOW?

1. What are the next two terms in the sequence? What is the 20th term in the sequence?

 Math Tools

 Online Practice

 Virtual Nerd Tutorials

2. Write the first four terms of a sequence so that the next two terms are 15 and 18.

3. You use 2 as a counterexample to verify that a classmate's conjecture is false. What is a possible conjecture your classmate made?

SOLVE IT!

The company that prints the bumper sticker at the left below accidentally reworded the original statement and printed the sticker three different ways. Suppose the original bumper sticker is true. Are the other bumper stickers true or false? Explain.

 Interactive Exploration

 Vocabulary Online

A **If you are too close, THEN YOU CAN READ THIS.**

B **If you cannot read this,** *then you are not too close.*

C **If you are not too close, THEN YOU CANNOT READ THIS.**

 Apply Mathematics (1)(A) Describe another real-world situation for which you could apply the same mathematical model.

Problem 1 | **Got It?** | Identifying the Hypothesis and the Conclusion

 Learning Animation

What are the hypothesis and the conclusion of the conditional?

If an angle measures 130, then the angle is obtuse.

 Problem 2 | **Got It?** | Writing a Conditional

 Learning Animation

How can you write "Dolphins are mammals" as a conditional?

Problem 3 | **Got It?** | Finding the Truth Value of a Conditional

 Learning Animation

Is the conditional *true* or *false*? If it is false, find a counterexample.

a. If a month has 28 days, then it is February.

b. If two angles form a linear pair, then they are supplementary.

 Problem 4 | **Got It?** | Identifying and Determining the Validity of Statements

Learning Animation

What are the converse, inverse, and contrapositive of the following conditional? What are the truth values of each? If a statement is false, give a counterexample.

If a vegetable is a carrot, then it contains beta carotene.

ELPS Read the solution to Problem 4 and take notes. Then use your notes about a conditional statement and its converse, inverse, and contrapositive to help you answer the Got It. Write another conditional statement about geometric figures and compare the truth values of the four statements.

Lesson Check

Do you know HOW?

Math Tools

Online Practice

Virtual Nerd Tutorials

1. What are the converse, inverse, and contrapositive of the statement? Which statements are true?

> If a figure is a rectangle with sides 2 cm and 3 cm, then it has a perimeter of 10 cm.

2. Write a conditional statement that matches the Venn diagram shown. Then write the converse of the statement and determine whether it is true.

3. The statement below is the inverse of a statement you read in your friend's math notebook. What is the statement in your friend's notebook? Is the statement true?

> If an angle is not acute, then the angle does not measure 45.

SOLVE IT!

Look at the examples of insects and noninsects below. How would you complete the following sentence: "If an animal is an insect, then . . . "? Explain your reasoning.

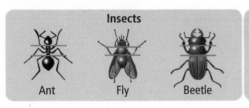

Interactive Exploration

Vocabulary Online

 Use Representations to Communicate Mathematical Ideas (1)(E)
Describe how the representation you used to solve the problem successfully organizes and communicates your ideas.

Problem 1 | **Got It?** | Writing a Biconditional

What is the converse of the following true conditional? If the converse is also true, rewrite the statements as a biconditional.

Learning
Animation

> If two angles have equal measure, then the angles are congruent.

TEKS Process Standard (1)(F)

 Problem 2 | **Got It?** | Identifying the Conditionals in a Biconditional

What are the two conditionals that form this biconditional?

Learning
Animation

> Two numbers are reciprocals if and only if their product is 1.

Problem 3 | **Got It?** | Writing a Definition as a Biconditional

Learning Animation

Is this definition of *straight angle* reversible? If yes, write it as a true biconditional.

Definition: A straight angle is an angle that measures 180.

 Problem 4 | **Got It?** | Identifying Good Definitions

Learning Animation

a. Is the following statement a good definition? Explain.

A square is a figure with four right angles.

b. How can you rewrite the statement "Obtuse angles have greater measures than acute angles" so that it is a good definition?

ELPS Read and discuss part (b) with a classmate. Tell why the given statement for obtuse angles is not a good definition. Then write a biconditional statement defining obtuse angles.

Lesson Check

Do you know HOW?

1. Write the following definition as a biconditional.

    Vertical angles are two angles whose sides are opposite rays.

2. A textbook contains the biconditional statement shown below. However, ink spilled on part of the statement. What words, numbers, or symbols are covered by the ink?

    $x =$ only if $3x + 2 = 11$.

3. Determine whether the following biconditional is true. Then write the two conditional statements that form the biconditional and determine whether they are true.

    You live in Albuquerque if and only if you live in New Mexico.

Math Tools

Online Practice

Virtual Nerd Tutorials

Lesson 2-3 │ Biconditionals and Definitions

46

SOLVE IT!

You want to use the coupon to buy three different pairs of jeans. You have narrowed your choices to four pairs. The costs of the different pairs are $24.99, $39.99, $40.99, and $50.00. If you spend as little as possible, what is the average amount per pair of jeans that you will pay? Explain.

Interactive Exploration

Vocabulary Online

BUY TWO PAIRS OF JEANS
Get a THIRD Free*

*Free jeans must be of equal or lesser value.

 Evaluate Reasonableness (1)(B) Explain how you know your solution is reasonable.

TEKS Process Standard (1)(G)

 Problem 1 | **Got It?** | Using the Law of Detachment

Learning Animation

What can you conclude from the given true statements?

a. If there is lightning, then it is not safe to be out in the open. Marla sees lightning from the soccer field.

b. If a figure is a square, then its sides have equal length. Figure *ABCD* has sides of equal length.

 Problem 2 | **Got It?** | Using the Law of Syllogism

Learning Animation

What can you conclude from the given information? What is your reasoning?

a. If a whole number ends in 0, then it is divisible by 10.
If a whole number is divisible by 10, then it is divisible by 5.

b. If $\overrightarrow{AB}$ and $\overrightarrow{AD}$ are opposite rays, then the two rays form a straight angle.
If two rays are opposite rays, then the two rays form a straight angle.

ELPS Listen as the teacher reads part (a). What letters can represent phrases in the statements? How can you write the statements using letters and symbols? Write the conclusion symbolically and in words.

Problem 3 **Got It?** Using the Laws of Syllogism and Detachment

Learning
Animation

a. What can you conclude from the given information? What is your reasoning?

If a river is more than 4000 mi long, then it is longer than the Amazon.

If a river is longer than the Amazon, then it is the longest river in the world.

The Nile is 4132 mi long.

b. In Problem 3, does it matter whether you use the Law of Syllogism or the Law of Detachment first? Explain.

Lesson Check

Do you know HOW?

Math Tools

Online Practice

Virtual Nerd Tutorials

1. If possible, make a conclusion from the given true statements. What reasoning did you use?

   If it is Saturday, then you walk to work.

   If you walk to work, then you wear sneakers.

2. Assume you can use Statement A, Statement B, and a law of deductive reasoning to write Statement C. What should Statement B be? Which law of deductive reasoning did you use?

   Statement A: If you catch the 8:05 bus, you arrive at school by 8:30.

   Statement B:

   Statement C: Zachary arrives at school by 8:30.

3. Write the contrapositive of each conditional statement. If possible, make a conclusion from the two contrapositives and state the law of deductive reasoning you used.

   If an animal is a poodle, then the animal is a dog.

   If an animal is a dog, then the animal is a mammal.

SOLVE IT!

Follow the steps of the brainteaser using your age. Then try it using a family member's age. What do you notice? Explain how the brainteaser works.

Interactive Exploration

Vocabulary Online

- Write down your age.
- Multiply it by 10.
- Add to the product.
- Double that answer and then subtract 16.
- Finally divide the result by 2.

 Use Multiple Representations to Communicate Mathematical Ideas (1)(D)
What is another representation you could you use to solve the problem? Explain why the representation would be useful.

Problem 1 **Got It?** **Justifying Steps When Solving an Equation**

TEKS Process Standard (1)(G)

What is the value of *x*? Justify each step.

Given: $\overrightarrow{AB}$ bisects $\angle RAN$.

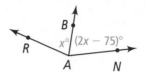

Learning Animation

 Problem 2 **Got It?** **Using Properties of Equality and Congruence**

For parts (a)–(c), what is the name of the property of equality or congruence that justifies going from the first statement to the second statement?

a. $\overline{AR} \cong \overline{TY}$
$\overline{TY} \cong \overline{AR}$

b. $3(x + 5) = 9$
$3x + 15 = 9$

c. $\frac{1}{4}x = 7$
$x = 28$

d. What property justifies the statement $m\angle R = m\angle R$?

Learning Animation

Lesson 2-5 | Reasoning in Algebra and Geometry

56

TEKS Process Standard (1)(E)

 Problem 3 | **Got It?** | Writing a Two-Column Proof

a. Write a two-column proof.

    Given: $\overline{AB} \cong \overline{CD}$

    Prove: $\overline{AC} \cong \overline{BD}$

Learning Animation

b. In Problem 3, why is Statement 2 necessary in the proof?

ELPS Point out $\overline{AC}$ and $\overline{BD}$ on the figure in part (a). What part do they have in common? What do you know about the other part of each segment? Use that information to write equations involving AC and BD. Use the equations in your proof.

Lesson Check

Do you know HOW?

Math Tools

Online Practice

Virtual Nerd Tutorials

1. Name the properties of equality that justify going from the first statement to the second statement and from the second statement to the third statement.

$$3x + x + 7 = 23$$

$$4x + 7 = 23$$

$$4x = 16$$

2. You can use the Addition Property of Equality to go from Statement A to Statement B. Write a statement that could be Statement A.

Statement A:

Statement B: $5x = 30$

3. The cost of ordering s sweatshirts online, including shipping, is modeled by the expression $18s + 7$. Your friend orders some sweatshirts for a school event and spends a total of $151. Write and solve an equation to find the number of sweatshirts he orders. Provide a reason for each step of the solution.

SOLVE IT!

A quilter wants to duplicate this quilt but knows the measures of only two angles. What are the measures of angles 1, 2, 3, and 4? How do you know?

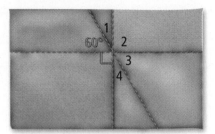

Interactive Exploration

Vocabulary Online

 Analyze Mathematical Relationships (1)(F) What mathematical relationships did you identify in the problem? How did you use them to solve the problem?

TEKS Process Standard (1)(D)

 Problem 1 | **Got It?** | **Proving the Vertical Angles Theorem**

Given: ∠2 and ∠4 are vertical angles.

Prove: ∠2 ≅ ∠4

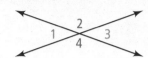

Learning Animation

 Problem 2 | **Got It?** | **Applying the Vertical Angles Theorem**

What is the value of *x*?

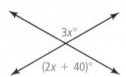

Learning Animation

Problem 3 | **Got It?** | **Writing a Proof Using the Vertical Angles Theorem**

a. Use the Vertical Angles Theorem to prove the following.

  Given: ∠1 ≅ ∠2

  Prove: ∠1 ≅ ∠2 ≅ ∠3 ≅ ∠4

Learning Animation

b. How can you prove ∠1 ≅ ∠2 ≅ ∠3 ≅ ∠4 without using the Vertical Angles Theorem? Explain.

Lesson 2-6 | Proving Angles Congruent

Problem 4 | Got It? | Distinguishing Between Mathematical Concepts

For each statement, determine whether it is an *undefined term,* a *definition,* a *postulate,* a *conjecture,* or a *theorem.*

I. If △*ABC* is a right triangle, then ∠*C* measures 90.

II. A point can be named by a capital letter, such as *A.*

III. A ray is part of a line that consists of one endpoint and all the points of the line on one side of the endpoint.

IV. If ∠1 and ∠2 are vertical angles, then they are congruent.

V. Through any two points *A* and *B,* there is exactly one line.

TEKS Process Standard (1)(G)

Problem 5 | Got It? | Writing a Paragraph Proof

Write a paragraph proof for the Vertical Angles Theorem.

 Draw two intersecting lines to form vertical angles. Label the angles 1, 2, 3, and 4. Discuss a strategy for proving that vertical angles are congruent before writing a paragraph proof. Underline the connecting words. Explain your proof to a classmate.

Do you know HOW?

1. What are the measures of ∠1, ∠2, and ∠3?

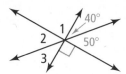

Math
Tools

Online
Practice

Virtual Nerd
Tutorials

2. ∠A is supplementary to ∠B and ∠C is supplementary to ∠B. Given that $m\angle C = x$, write algebraic expressions for $m\angle A$ and $m\angle B$.

3. A lamp is mounted on an extendable arm, as shown. You know that ∠2 ≅ ∠3 and ∠4 ≅ ∠5. Explain how you can prove that ∠1 ≅ ∠6. Provide a reason for each step.

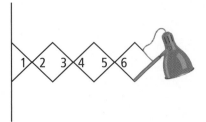

PearsonTEXAS.com

You want to assemble a bookcase. You have all the pieces, but you misplaced the instructions that came with the box. How would you write the instructions?

Interactive Exploration

Vocabulary Online

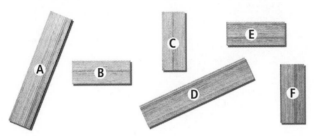

 Create Representations to Communicate Mathematical Ideas (1)(E)
Describe how the representation you made successfully organizes and communicates your solution to the problem.

Problem 1 | **Got It?** | Identifying Nonintersecting Lines and Planes

In the figure, assume that lines and planes that appear to be parallel are parallel.

Learning
Animation

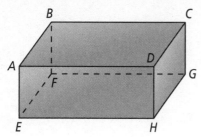

a. Which segments are parallel to $\overline{AD}$?

b. Explain why $\overline{FE}$ and $\overline{CD}$ are *not* skew.

c. In Problem 1, you found plane *ABCD* ∥ plane *EFGH* and plane *DCG* ∥ plane *ABF*. What is another pair of parallel planes?

d. What are two segments parallel to plane *DCGH*?

ELPS Discuss what you heard about parallel planes in the lesson. How many planes that are not parallel can you visualize between different pairs of parallel edges in this diagram? Discuss your conclusion with a classmate.

Problem 2 | Got It? | Identifying an Angle Pair

What are three pairs of corresponding angles?

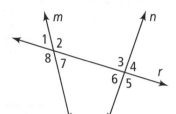

Learning
Animation

 Problem 3 | Got It? | Classifying an Angle Pair

In Problem 3, are angles 1 and 3 *alternate interior angles, same-side interior angles, corresponding angles,* or *alternate exterior angles*?

Learning
Animation

Lesson Check

Do you know HOW?

1. Name one pair of each of the following. Lines and planes that appear to be parallel are parallel.

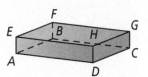

   a. parallel segments

   b. skew segments

   c. parallel planes

2. Draw a pair of non-parallel lines and a transversal. Using numbers, label each angle. Name a pair of corresponding angles, a pair of same-side interior angles, and a pair of alternate interior angles.

3. Which of the following pairs of angles are alternate interior angles? Explain your answer by naming the two lines and transversal that form the pair.

   ∠2 and ∠3, ∠1 and ∠4, ∠2 and ∠7

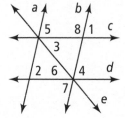

SOLVE IT!

Look at the map of streets in Clearwater, Florida. Nicholson Street and Cedar Street are parallel. Which pairs of angles appear to be congruent?

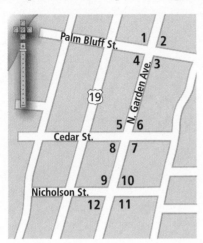

 Interactive Exploration

 Vocabulary Online

 Connect Mathematical Ideas (1)(F) What prior knowledge did you draw on to solve the problem?

Problem 1 | **Got It?** | Investigating Patterns in Geometric Relationships

Parallel lines *a* and *b* are cut by a transversal as shown. Measure the angles formed. Based on your measurements, make a conjecture about how alternate exterior angles are related when parallel lines are cut by a transversal.

Learning Animation

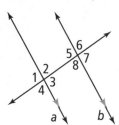

TEKS Process Standard (1)(G)

 Problem 2 | **Got It?** | Identifying Supplementary Angles

If you know the measure of one of the angles, can you always find the measures of all eight angles when two parallel lines are cut by a transversal? Explain.

Learning Animation

Problem 3 | Got It? | Proving the Alternate Interior Angles Theorem

Write a paragraph proof to prove the Alternate Interior Angles
Theorem (Theorem 3-1).

Given: $c \parallel d$

Prove: $\angle 4 \cong \angle 6$

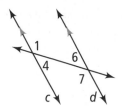

Learning
Animation

Problem 4 | Got It? | Proving an Angle Relationship

Given: $a \parallel b$

Prove: $\angle 1 \cong \angle 7$

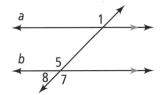

Learning
Animation

Problem 5 | **Got It?** | **Finding Measures of Angles**

What is the measure of each angle? Which theorem or postulate justifies each answer?

Learning Animation

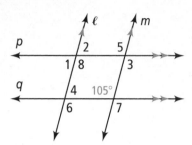

a. ∠1

b. ∠2

c. ∠5

d. ∠6

e. ∠7

f. ∠8

ELPS Describe the diagram. What information do the arrows give? What is the meaning of the expression heard in this lesson "lines *p* and *q* are cut by the transversal *m*?"

Problem 6 | **Got It?** | **Finding an Angle Measure**

Learning
Animation

a. In the figure, what are the values of *x* and *y*?

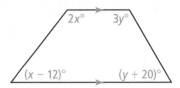

b. What are the measures of the four angles in the figure above?

Lesson Check

Math Tools

Online Practice

Virtual Nerd Tutorials

Do you know HOW?

1. If $m\angle 1 = 70$, what is $m\angle 8$? Explain.

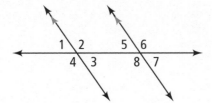

2. If $m\angle 6 = 5x - 1$ and $m\angle 3 = 11x + 5$, what is the value of x? Find $m\angle 6$ and $m\angle 3$.

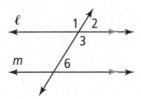

3. If $m\angle 3$ is 6 less than twice $m\angle 5$, what is $m\angle 2$? Explain your reasoning.

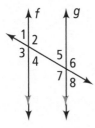

3-3 Proving Lines Parallel

PearsonTEXAS.com

SOLVE IT!

The maze below has two intersecting sets of parallel paths. A mouse makes five turns in the maze to get to a piece of cheese. Follow the mouse's path through the maze. What is the number of degrees at each turn? Explain how you know.

Interactive Exploration

Vocabulary Online

 Connect Mathematical Ideas (1)(F) How does this problem relate to a problem you have seen before?

Problem 1 | Got It? | Using a Flow Chart to Prove Theorem 3-7

In Problem 1, you used the diagram shown to prove
Theorem 3-7. Use the same diagram to prove Theorem 3-6.

Given: $m\angle 3 + m\angle 6 = 180$

Prove: $\ell \parallel m$

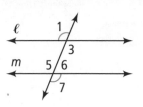

Problem 2 | Got It? | Identifying Parallel Lines

Which lines are parallel if $\angle 6 \cong \angle 7$? Justify your answer.

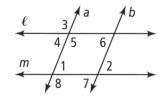

Lesson 3-3 | Proving Lines Parallel

82

Problem 3 **Got It?** **Determining Whether Lines Are Parallel**

In Problem 3, what is another way to explain why $r \parallel s$? Justify your answer.

Learning Animation

ELPS The new theorems heard in this lesson are converses of those learned earlier in the topic. Discuss with a classmate how a converse changes the word order of the original statement. Then listen to your partner explain a theorem that can be used to solve the Got It. Find another theorem and exchange roles.

Problem 4 **Got It?** **Using Algebra**

What is the value of w for which $c \parallel d$?

Learning Animation

55°   c

$(3w - 2)°$ d

Lesson Check

Do you know HOW?

1. Which theorem or postulate proves that $a \parallel b$?

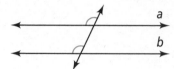

Math
Tools

Online
Practice

Virtual Nerd
Tutorials

2. Which lines are parallel if $\angle 3$ and $\angle 6$ are supplementary? Justify your conclusion.

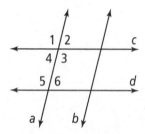

3. What is the value of x for which $m \parallel n$?

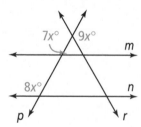

SOLVE IT!

Jude and Jasmine leave school together to walk home. Jasmine cuts down a path from Schoolhouse Road to get to Oak Street, and Jude cuts down another path to get to Court Road. Below is a diagram of the route each follows home. What conjecture can you make about Oak Street and Court Road? Explain.

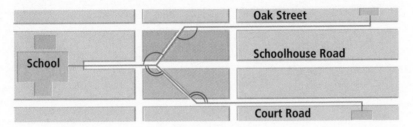

Interactive Exploration

Vocabulary Online

 Use Representations to Communicate Mathematical Ideas (1)(E)
Describe how the representation you used to solve the problem successfully organizes and communicates your ideas.

TEKS Process Standard (1)(A)

 Problem 1 | **Got It?** | Solving a Problem With Parallel Lines

Can you assemble the pieces below to form a picture frame with opposite sides parallel? Explain.

Learning Animation

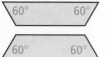 

Lesson 3-4 | Parallel and Perpendicular Lines

Problem 2 | **Got It?** | Proving a Relationship Between Two Lines

Given: In a plane, $c \perp b$, $b \perp d$, and $d \perp a$.

Prove: $a \parallel b$

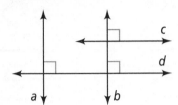

Learning
Animation

ELPS Discuss with a classmate the steps you could take to try to show that line a is
parallel to line b. Write a paragraph proof, being as specific and detailed
as possible.

Lesson Check

Do you know HOW?

Math
Tools

Online
Practice

Virtual Nerd
Tutorials

1. In the diagram below, lines *a, b,* and *c* are coplanar. What conclusion can you make about lines *a* and *b*? How can you justify your conclusion?

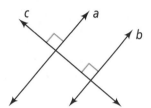

2. Main Street intersects Avenue A and Avenue B. Avenue A is parallel to Avenue B. What conditions must be true for Avenue B to be perpendicular to Main Street? Explain.

3. Nick built a bookcase similar to the drawing at the right. How can he use right angles to make sure that the two vertical sides are parallel to each other? How can he use right angles to make sure that the shelves are parallel to each other? Which theorem justifies his method?

1		7
2		8
3		9
4		10
5		11
6		12

SOLVE IT!

What is the sum of the angle measures of each triangle? Explain. (*Hint:* Rearrange the corners of each triangle.) Suppose you have a third triangle. Make a conjecture about the sum of the angle measures of the third triangle.

Interactive
Exploration

Vocabulary
Online

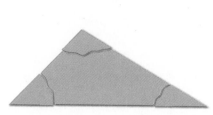

 Select Techniques to Solve Problems (1)(C) What other techniques could you use to solve the problem? Select one and explain how you would use it.

TEKS Process Standard (1)(G)

 Problem 1 **Got It?** Proving the Triangle Angle-Sum Theorem

Learning Animation

Without using $\angle XZB$, prove the Triangle Angle-Sum Theorem (Theorem 3-11).

Given: $\triangle XYZ$, $\overline{AB} \parallel \overline{XY}$

Prove: $m\angle X + m\angle 2 + m\angle Y = 180$

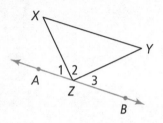

TEKS Process Standard (1)(F)

 Problem 2 **Got It?** Using the Triangle Angle-Sum Theorem

Learning Animation

What is the value of z in the diagram below?

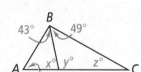

Problem 3 | **Got It?** | Using the Triangle Exterior Angle Theorem

Learning
Animation

Two angles of a triangle each measure 53. What is the measure of an exterior angle at each vertex of the triangle?

 Read the Got It. What is the difference between interior and exterior angles? Write these terms on flashcards and practice identifying them by sight. Draw the triangle described and label both types of angles. Reread the Triangle Exterior Angle Theorem and then find the missing measurements in your triangle.

 Problem 4 | **Got It?** | Applying the Triangle Theorems

Learning
Animation

In Problem 4, can you find $m\angle A$ without using the Triangle Exterior Angle Theorem? Explain.

Lesson 3-5 | Parallel Lines and Triangles

Lesson Check

Do you know HOW?

For Exercises 1–3, use the diagram at the right.

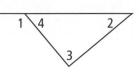

Math
Tools

Online
Practice

Virtual Nerd
Tutorials

1. Given that $m\angle 1 = 120$ and $m\angle 2 = 35$, find $m\angle 3$.

2. If $\angle 3$ is a right angle, $m\angle 4 = 5x - 6$, and $m\angle 2 = 3x$, what are the measures of $\angle 1$, $\angle 2$, and $\angle 4$?

3. Suppose $m\angle 1$ is 5 times $m\angle 2$, and $m\angle 3$ is 30 more than one-half of $m\angle 1$. What are the measures of all four angles?

SOLVE IT!

Draw a line *m* on a sheet of paper. Fold your paper so that line *m* falls on itself. Label your fold line *n*. Fold your paper again so that *n* falls on itself. Label your new fold line *p*.

How are *m* and *p* related? How do you know?

Interactive Exploration

Vocabulary Online

 Explain Mathematical Ideas (1)(G) A classmate questions your solution to the problem. Use precise mathematical language to explain why your solution is correct.

Problem 1 | **Got It?** | **Constructing Parallel Lines**

In Problem 1, you constructed line *m* through point *N* with *m* ∥ ℓ. Why must lines ℓ and *m* be parallel?

Learning Animation

TEKS Process Standard (1)(C)

 Problem 2 | **Got It?** | **Constructing a Special Quadrilateral**

a. Draw a segment. Label its length *m*. Construct quadrilateral *ABCD* with
$\overleftrightarrow{AB} \parallel \overleftrightarrow{CD}$, so that *AB* = *m* and *CD* = 2*m*.

Learning Animation

b. Suppose you and a friend both use the steps in Problem 2 to construct *ABYZ* independently. Will your quadrilaterals necessarily have the same angle measures and side lengths? Explain.

Lesson 3-6 | Constructing Parallel and Perpendicular Lines

Problem 3 | Got It? | Perpendicular at a Point on a Line

Use a compass and straightedge. Draw $\overleftrightarrow{EF}$. Construct $\overleftrightarrow{FG}$ so that $\overleftrightarrow{FG} \perp \overleftrightarrow{EF}$ at point F.

Learning Animation

TEKS Process Standard (1)(E)

Problem 4 | Got It? | Perpendicular From a Point to a Line

Use a compass and straightedge. Draw $\overleftrightarrow{CX}$ and a point Z not on $\overleftrightarrow{CX}$. Construct $\overleftrightarrow{ZB}$ so that $\overleftrightarrow{ZB} \perp \overleftrightarrow{CX}$.

Learning Animation

ELPS Draw a line and a point not on the line. Listen to your classmate describe the strategy for drawing a line, through the point, that is perpendicular to the line. Follow the directions and complete specific steps with a compass and straightedge. Label the parts of the figure. Then exchange roles.

Do you know HOW?

1. Use a straightedge and compass. Draw a line ℓ and a point P not on the line. Construct the line through point P parallel to line ℓ.

Math
Tools

Online
Practice

Virtual Nerd
Tutorials

2. Using $\overline{AB}$ below, construct $\overline{BC}$ so that it is perpendicular to $\overline{AB}$. Construct $\overline{CD}$ so that it is perpendicular to $\overline{BC}$.

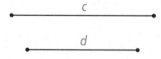

3. Use a straightedge and compass. Construct a rectangle with sides of length c and d.

Lesson Check

Do you UNDERSTAND?

4. Analyze Mathematical Relationships (1)(F) In Exercise 2, what is the relationship between $\overline{AB}$ and $\overline{CD}$? Which theorem justifies your conclusion?

Math Tools

Online Practice

Virtual Nerd Tutorials

5. Select Tools to Solve Problems (1)(C) Suppose you use a wider compass setting in Step 1 of Problem 4. Will you construct a different perpendicular line? Explain.

6. Connect Mathematical Ideas (1)(F) How are the constructions in Problems 3 and 4 similar? How are they different?

TEXAS Test Practice

Multiple Choice

For Exercises 1–3, choose the correct letter.

1. Your teacher tells you to construct a line parallel to a given line through point *N* not on the line. Using a compass and a straightedge, which diagram below shows the first step of your construction?

   A.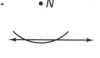

   B.

   C.

   D.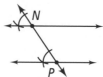

2. Elisa's dog ate her homework. Elisa thinks she can match sketches from the scrap paper she used so she doesn't have to start over. What kind of line was Elisa constructing in this series of diagrams?

   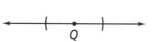 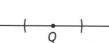 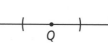

   F. parallel   **G.** perpendicular   **H.** congruent   **J.** similar

3. Which diagram below shows line *m* parallel to line *n*?

   A.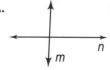

   B.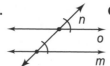

   C.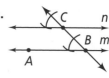

   D.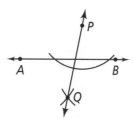

Short Response

4. Explain the error in the construction shown. The student is attempting to draw a perpendicular line through a point not on the line.

3-7 Equations of Lines in the Coordinate Plane

 SOLVE IT!

Ski resorts often use steepness to rate the difficulty of their hills. The steeper the hill, the higher the difficulty rating. Below are sketches of the three new hills at a particular resort. Use each rating level only once. Which hill gets which rating? Explain.

Difficulty Ratings

● Easiest

■ Intermediate

◆ Difficult

Interactive Exploration

Vocabulary Online

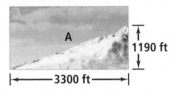

A   1190 ft

|←——3300 ft——→|

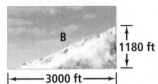

B   1180 ft

|←——3000 ft——→|

C   1150 ft

|←——3500 ft——→|

Connect Mathematical Ideas (1)(F) What prior knowledge did you draw on to solve the problem?

TEKS Process Standard (1)(D)

 Problem 1 | **Got It?** | Deriving the Slope Formula

 Learning Animation

In Problem 1, you derived the slope formula by dividing the vertical change from point (x_1, y_1) to point (x_2, y_2) by the horizontal change. Does it matter from which point you choose to subtract the values of the coordinates? Explain your reasoning.

 Problem 2 | **Got It?** | Finding Slopes of Lines

Learning Animation

Use the graph at the right.

a. What is the slope of line *a*?

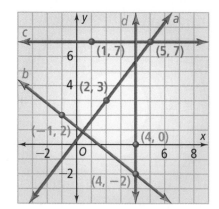

b. What is the slope of line *c*?

TEKS Process Standard (1)(E)

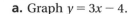 **Problem 3** | **Got It?** | Graphing Lines

Learning Animation

a. Graph $y = 3x - 4$.

b. Graph $y - 2 = -\frac{1}{3}(x - 4)$.

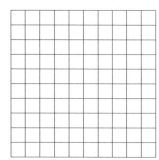 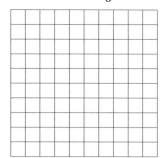

Problem 4 | **Got It?** | **Writing Equations of Lines**

Learning
Animation

a. What is an equation of the line with slope $-\frac{1}{2}$ and *y*-intercept 2?

b. What is an equation of the line through $(-1, 4)$ with slope -3?

 Using vocabulary from the lesson, explain to your partner how you would solve part (a). Then, listen as your partner narrates how she or he would solve part (b).

Problem 5 | **Got It?** | **Using Two Points to Write an Equation**

Learning
Animation

a. In Problem 5, you used the point $(3, 5)$ in the last step. What is the equation of the line if you use $(-2, -1)$ instead?

b. Rewrite the equations in Problem 5 and part (a) in slope-intercept form and compare them. What can you conclude?

Problem 6 | **Got It?** | **Writing Equations of Horizontal and Vertical Lines**

Learning
Animation

a. What are the equations for the horizontal and vertical lines through $(4, -3)$?

b. Can you write the equation of a vertical line in slope-intercept form? Explain.

Lesson 3-7 | **Equations of Lines in the Coordinate Plane**

107

Lesson Check

Do you know HOW?

1. What is the slope of the line passing through the points (4, 5) and (6, 15)?

Math Tools

Online Practice

Virtual Nerd Tutorials

2. Write an equation in slope-intercept form of a line that has a *y*-intercept of −6 and the same slope as the line graphed below.

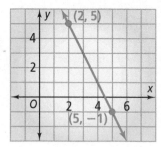

3. What is an equation of the line passing through points (3, 3) and (4, 7)? Write the equation in both point-slope form and slope-intercept form.

SOLVE IT!

You and a friend enjoy exercising together. One day, you are about to go running when your friend receives a phone call. You decide to start running and tell your friend to catch up after the call. The red line represents you, and the blue line represents your friend. Will your friend catch up? Explain.

Interactive Exploration

Vocabulary Online

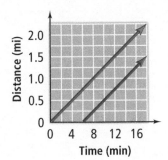

 Apply Mathematics (1)(A) Describe another real-world situation for which you could apply the same mathematical model.

Problem 1 | Got It? | Verifying Parallelism

Learning Animation

Line ℓ_3 contains $A(-13, 6)$ and $B(-1, 2)$. Line ℓ_4 contains $C(3, 6)$ and $D(6, 7)$.
Are ℓ_3 and ℓ_4 parallel? Explain.

TEKS Process Standard (1)(G)

Problem 2 | Got It? | Writing Equations of Parallel Lines

Learning Animation

What is an equation of the line parallel to $y = -x - 7$ that contains $(-5, 3)$?

Problem 3 | **Got It?** | Verifying Perpendicularity

Line ℓ_3 contains $A(2, 7)$ and $B(3, -1)$. Line ℓ_4 contains $C(-2, 6)$ and $D(8, 7)$. Are ℓ_3 and ℓ_4 perpendicular? Explain.

Learning Animation

TEKS Process Standard (1)(B)

 Problem 4 | **Got It?** | Writing Equations of Perpendicular Lines

Use the diagram in Problem 3. Suppose a second player standing at (90, 40) misses the ball, turns around, and runs on a path parallel to the baseball's path. What is an equation of the line representing this player's path?

Learning Animation

ELPS Discuss with a classmate how to find the slope of a line. Then discuss any prior experience you have with the game of baseball. Use this information to read and solve the Got It together.

Lesson 3-8 | Slopes of Parallel and Perpendicular Lines

Lesson Check

Do you know HOW?

1. $\overleftrightarrow{AB}$ contains points $A(-8, 3)$ and $B(-4, 11)$. $\overleftrightarrow{CD}$ contains points $C(-1, 3)$ and $D(1, 2)$. Are $\overleftrightarrow{AB}$ and $\overleftrightarrow{CD}$ *parallel, perpendicular,* or *neither*? Explain.

Math Tools

Online Practice

Virtual Nerd Tutorials

2. The four-sided figure *PQRS* has parallel sides $\overline{PQ}$ and $\overline{RS}$. If *PQRS* has vertices $P(3, z)$, $Q(2, -1)$, $R(7, -2)$, and $S(10, 16)$, what is the value of z? Explain the method you used to solve the problem.

3. Line ℓ_1 is perpendicular to $y = -4x + 1$ and contains the point $(2, -3)$. Line ℓ_2 is parallel to $y = -4x + 1$ and contains the point $(2, -3)$. Write the equations for ℓ_1 and ℓ_2 in slope-intercept form. How are ℓ_1 and ℓ_2 related? Explain.

SOLVE IT!

You can use latitude and longitude to identify positions on Earth. Look at the latitude and longitude markings on the globe. Think about "slicing" the globe with a plane at each latitude. Which of your slices contain the center of the globe, if any? What if you slice the globe with a plane at each longitude?

Interactive Exploration

Vocabulary Online

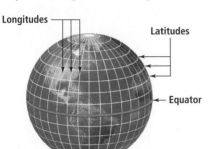

Longitudes

Latitudes

Equator

 Explain Mathematical Ideas (1)(G) A classmate questions your solution to the problem. Use precise mathematical language to explain why your solution is correct.

TEKS Process Standard (1)(D)

 Problem 1 | **Got It?** | Comparing Lines in Euclidean and Spherical Geometries

Learning Animation

Explain the differences between a line in Euclidean geometry and a line in spherical geometry. Draw a sketch to support your answer.

 Mark two points on a ball and indicate the line that they define in spherical geometry. Discuss with your partner why there are no parallel lines in spherical geometry. Be sure to use key vocabulary words and expressions such as *parallel to*, *line*, *spherical*, and *intersect*.

 Problem 2 | **Got It?** | Sums of Angle Measures of Triangles

Learning Animation

What is the sum of the measures of the angles of triangle *ABC*? Could a triangle exist with these angle measures in Euclidean geometry? Explain.

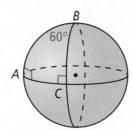

Problem 3 | Got It? | Using the Spherical Geometry Triangle Angle-Sum Theorem

The three angle measures of a triangle are 78, 92, and 88. Does the triangle exist in Euclidean geometry, spherical geometry, or neither? Explain.

Learning Animation

TEKS Process Standard (1)(G)

Problem 4 | Got It? | Comparing Spherical and Euclidean Geometries

The following postulate holds in Euclidean geometry. Does it hold in spherical geometry? Explain.

Learning Animation

If two points lie in a plane, then the line containing those points lies in the plane.

Do you know HOW?

1. The angle measures of a triangle are 25, 85, and 80. Does this triangle exist in Euclidean geometry, spherical geometry, or neither? Explain.

Math
Tools

Online
Practice

Virtual Nerd
Tutorials

2. Consider two points on opposite ends of a sphere. How many line segments in Euclidean geometry can you draw that connect these two points? How many line segments in spherical geometry can you draw? Explain.

3. In Euclidean geometry, the only possible equiangular triangle has three 60° angles. Draw a counterexample to illustrate that this property does not apply to spherical geometry.

SOLVE IT!

You are working on a puzzle. You've almost finished, except for a few pieces of the sky. Place the remaining pieces in the puzzle. How did you figure out where to place the pieces?

Interactive Exploration

Vocabulary Online

 Select Techniques to Solve Problems (1)(C) What other techniques could you use to solve the problem? Select one and explain how you would use it.

Problem 1 **Got It?** **Finding Congruent Sides and Angles**

If $\triangle WYS \cong \triangle MKV$, what are the congruent corresponding parts?

Learning
Animation

TEKS Process Standard (1)(B)

 Problem 2 **Got It?** **Using Congruent Sides and Angles**

Suppose that $\triangle WYS \cong \triangle MKV$. If $m\angle W = 62$ and $m\angle Y = 35$, what is $m\angle V$?
Explain.

Learning
Animation

Lesson 4-1 | **Congruent Figures**

124

TEKS Process Standard (1)(G)

 Problem 3 | **Got It?** | **Finding Congruent Triangles**

Is $\triangle ABD \cong \triangle CBD$? Justify your answer.

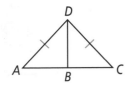

 Learning Animation

 Problem 4 | **Got It?** | **Proving Triangles Congruent**

Given: $\angle A \cong \angle D$, $\overline{AE} \cong \overline{DC}$,
$\overline{EB} \cong \overline{CB}$, $\overline{BA} \cong \overline{BD}$

Prove: $\triangle AEB \cong \triangle DCB$

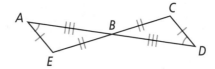

Learning Animation

ELPS With a classmate, read the Got It and discuss the steps you would take to solve this problem. Write your proof, then exchange papers and read your partner's work. Provide feedback on what you read, confirming agreement and providing support to make any needed changes.

Lesson Check

Do you know HOW?

1. Complete the following statements.

   Given: $\triangle BAT \cong \triangle FOR$

   a. $\overline{TA} \cong$ _____

   b. $\angle R \cong$ _____

2. **Given:** $\triangle CON \cong \triangle GRU$, $m\angle C = 23$, $m\angle O = 58$

   What is the measure of $\angle U$?

3. **Given:** $\triangle TRI \cong \triangle ANG$, $TR = 4x - 1$, $AN = 2x + 7$, and $AG = 3x + 4$

   a. Find the value of x.

   b. Find TI.

SOLVE IT!

Select a tool, such as a compass, ruler, or tracing paper, to help you accurately compare the two triangles below. Are they congruent? Describe the method you used.

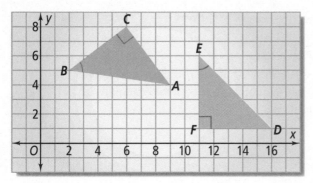

Interactive Exploration

Vocabulary Online

Analyze Mathematical Relationships (1)(F) What mathematical relationships did you identify in the problem? How did you use them to solve the problem?

TEKS Process Standard (1)(C)

 Problem 1 Got It? Building Triangles

Select objects of the same length, such as toothpicks, to solve the problem.

Learning
Animation

a. Build a triangle with a certain number of toothpicks for each side.

b. Build at least two more triangles with side lengths that use the same number of toothpicks. Compare the triangles. Make a conjecture about two triangles in which corresponding sides are congruent.

TEKS Process Standard (1)(E)

 Problem 2 Got It? Using SSS

Given: $\overline{BC} \cong \overline{BF}$, $\overline{CD} \cong \overline{FD}$

Prove: $\triangle BCD \cong \triangle BFD$

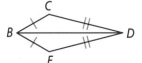

Learning
Animation

Lesson 4-2 | Triangle Congruence by SSS and SAS

130

Problem 3 | **Got It?** | **Using SAS**

What other information do you need to prove $\triangle LEB \cong \triangle BNL$ by SAS?

Learning Animation

 Problem 4 | **Got It?** | **Identifying Congruent Triangles**

Would you use SSS or SAS to prove the triangles congruent? Explain.

Learning Animation

ELPS Describe the SSS Postulate to a partner and listen as he or she describes the SAS Postulate. Then use these terms as well as other math vocabulary to explain which method should be used to solve the problem.

Lesson Check

Do you know HOW?

1. In △*HAT*, between which sides is the given angle included?

   a. ∠*H*

   b. ∠*T*

Math Tools

Online Practice

Virtual Nerd Tutorials

2. For what value of *x* could you use the SAS Postulate to prove that △*JKM* ≅ △*LKM*? Explain.

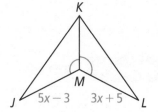

3. In the diagram, $\overrightarrow{WY}$ bisects ∠*XWZ*, and $\overline{WX} \cong \overline{WZ}$.

   a. Prove that the two triangles are congruent.

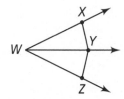

   b. Does it matter where point *Y* is located on $\overrightarrow{WY}$? Explain your answer.

Lesson 4-2 | Triangle Congruence by SSS and SAS

132

SOLVE IT!

Oh no! The school's photocopier is not working correctly. The copies all have some ink missing. Below are two photocopies of the same geometry worksheet. Which triangles are congruent? How do you know?

Copy 1

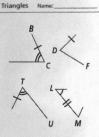

Copy 2

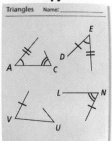

Interactive Exploration

Vocabulary Online

Use a Problem-Solving Model (1)(B) Evaluate your problem-solving model. Which parts were helpful? Which would you want to revise? Explain.

Problem 1 | **Got It?** | **Using ASA**

Learning Animation

Which two triangles are congruent by ASA? Explain.

 Problem 2 | **Got It?** | **Writing a Proof Using ASA**

Learning Animation

Given: $\angle CAB \cong \angle DAE$, $\overline{BA} \cong \overline{EA}$,
$\angle B$ and $\angle E$ are right angles

Prove: $\triangle ABC \cong \triangle AED$

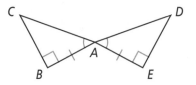

ELPS Discuss with a partner the kinds of questions that prompt the most information.
Then ask your partner one question that will help you complete the Got It.

Problem 3 | **Got It?** | **Writing a Proof Using AAS**

a. Given: $\angle S \cong \angle Q$, $\overline{RP}$ bisects $\angle SRQ$

Prove: $\triangle SRP \cong \triangle QRP$

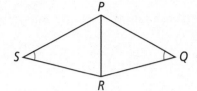

 Learning Animation

b. In Problem 3, you proved that $\triangle WMR \cong \triangle RKW$ by AAS. How could you prove the triangles congruent by ASA? Explain.

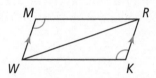

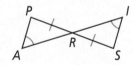 **Problem 4** | **Got It?** | **Determining Whether Triangles Are Congruent**

Are $\triangle PAR$ and $\triangle SIR$ congruent? Explain.

 Learning Animation

Do you know HOW?

1. Which postulate or theorem could you use to prove $\triangle ABC \cong \triangle DEF$?

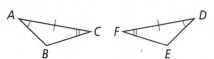

Math Tools

Online Practice

Virtual Nerd Tutorials

2. The top and bottom of this building truss are parallel. What additional information do you need to prove $\triangle ABC \cong \triangle DCB$ by ASA? What value of x would make the triangles congruent?

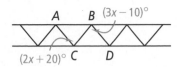

3. In $\triangle ABC$, $\overline{BD}$ is perpendicular to $\overline{AC}$. Are $\triangle ABD$ and $\triangle CBD$ congruent? Justify your answer.

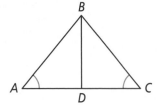

Scan page for an interactive
version of this Solve It.

In the object shown, flat wooden bars are joined together at the endpoints by single pins. The pins allow the bars to swivel around their points of intersection. Bars of the same color have the same length. Prove that if the angles labeled 1 are congruent, then all the other numbered pairs of angles are congruent.

Interactive
Exploration

Vocabulary
Online

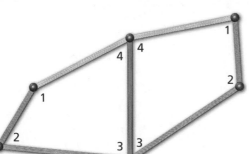

Analyze Mathematical Relationships (1)(F) What mathematical relationships did you identify in the problem? How did you use them to solve the problem?

Problem 1 | **Got It?** | **Proving Parts of Triangles Congruent**

Given: $\overline{BA} \cong \overline{DA}$, $\overline{CA} \cong \overline{EA}$

Prove: $\angle C \cong \angle E$

Learning
Animation

Lesson 4-4 | Using Corresponding Parts of Congruent Triangles

142

TEKS Process Standard (1)(G)

 Problem 2 **Got It?** Proving Triangle Parts Congruent to
Measure Distance

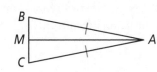

Learning
Animation

a. Given: $\overline{AB} \cong \overline{AC}$, M is the midpoint of $\overline{BC}$

Prove: $\angle AMB \cong \angle AMC$

b. Problem 2 describes how Thales aligned one stick of his compass with a ship
and then found a landmark on the shore with the same alignment. If the
landmark were not at sea level, would his method still work? Explain.

ELPS Discuss with a classmate how the diagram for the Got It is similar to the
illustration shown for Problem 2. Use this information to solve part (a) together.

Lesson Check

Do you know HOW?

1. Name the postulate or theorem that you can use to show the triangles are congruent. Then explain why $\overline{EA} \cong \overline{MA}$.

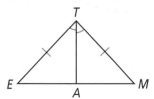

2. If $\overline{KN}$ and $\overline{LM}$ bisect each other, prove that $\overline{KL}$ and $\overline{MN}$ are parallel.

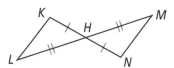

3. Use the fact that $\overline{BD}$ is a perpendicular bisector of $\overline{AC}$ to prove that $\angle A \cong \angle C$.

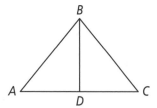

SOLVE IT!

The triangles of the same color are congruent. Arrange the triangles to form one large triangle. You must use all the pieces. Make a sketch of this triangle. Classify this triangle by its sides. What are the angle measures of this triangle? Explain.

Interactive Exploration

Vocabulary Online

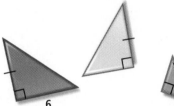 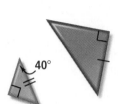 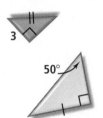

40°

3

50°

6

 Create Representations to Communicate Mathematical Ideas (1)(E)
Describe how the representation you made successfully organizes and communicates your solution to the problem.

TEKS Process Standard (1)(C)

Problem 1 | Got It? | Using Constructions of Congruent Segments

Construct $\angle ABC$ and then draw $\overline{AC}$. Make a separate triangle by constructing $\overline{XY}$ congruent to $\overline{AC}$, then sides $\overline{XZ}$ and $\overline{YZ}$ congruent to $\overline{AB}$ and $\overline{BC}$, respectively. Make a conjecture about two triangles whose corresponding sides are congruent.

Learning Animation

Problem 2 | Got It? | Proving the Isosceles Triangle Theorem

Rewrite the two-column proof of the Isosceles Triangle Theorem as a paragraph proof.

Learning Animation

Problem 3 **Got It?** Using the Isosceles Triangle Theorem and Its Converse

Learning Animation

a. Is ∠*WVS* congruent to ∠*S*? Is $\overline{TR}$ congruent to $\overline{TS}$? Explain.

b. Can you conclude that △*RUV* is isosceles? Explain.

 ELPS Explain the Isosceles Triangle Theorem to a partner. Restate any mispronounced words or incomplete statements, asking your partner for help as needed. Then switch roles and have your partner explain the Converse of the Isosceles Triangle Theorem.

 Problem 4 **Got It?** Using Algebra

Learning Animation

What is the value of *x*?

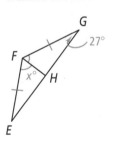

TEKS Process Standard (1)(G)

Problem 5 **Got It?** Finding Angle Measures

Learning Animation

Suppose the triangles in Problem 5 are isosceles triangles, where ∠*ADE*, ∠*DEC*, and ∠*ECB* are vertex angles, as shown below. If the vertex angles each have a measure of 58, what are *m*∠*A* and *m*∠*BCD*?

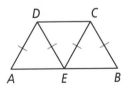

Do you know HOW?

Math Tools

Online Practice

Virtual Nerd Tutorials

1. The measure of one base angle of an isosceles triangle is 23. What are the measures of the other two angles?

2. What is the value of x?

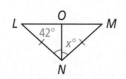

3. If $m\angle CAB = 70$, $\overline{AB} \cong \overline{BC}$, and ℓ and m are parallel lines, what is $m\angle CDE$?

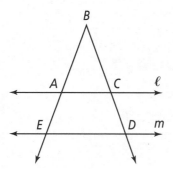

SOLVE IT!

One of the tent flaps was damaged in a storm. Can you use the other flap as a pattern to replace it? Explain.

Interactive Exploration

Vocabulary Online

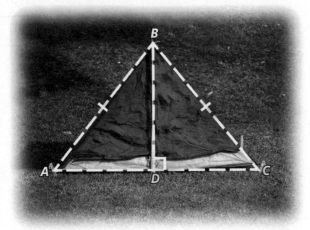

 Connect Mathematical Ideas (1)(F) How does this problem relate to a problem you have seen before?

Problem 1 | **Got It?** | **Using the HL Theorem**

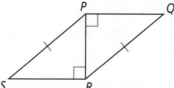

a. **Given:** ∠PRS and ∠RPQ are right angles, $\overline{SP} \cong \overline{QR}$

   Prove: △PRS ≅ △RPQ

b. Your friend says, "Suppose you have two right triangles with congruent hypotenuses and one pair of congruent legs. It does not matter which leg in the first triangle is congruent to which leg in the second triangle. The triangles will be congruent." Is your friend correct? Explain.

ELPS Read part (b) with a partner. Which vocabulary words did you recognize right away? Which words do you use routinely in class? Paraphrase this question in your own words.

Problem 2 | **Got It?** | Writing a Proof Using the HL Theorem

Learning
Animation

Given: $\overline{CD} \cong \overline{EA}$, $\overline{AD}$ is the perpendicular bisector of $\overline{CE}$

Prove: $\triangle CBD \cong \triangle EBA$

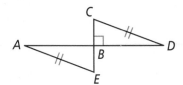

Lesson Check

Do you know HOW?

Math
Tools

Online
Practice

Virtual Nerd
Tutorials

1. Are the two triangles congruent? If so, write the congruence statement.

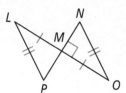

2. For what values of x and y are the triangles below congruent by HL?

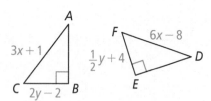

3. What other information do you need in order to prove $\triangle GHI \cong \triangle GJI$ by the HL Theorem?

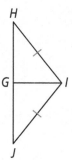

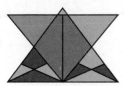

An assignment for your graphic design class is to make a colorful design using triangles. How many triangles are in your design? Explain how you count them.

Interactive Exploration

Vocabulary Online

 Use Multiple Representations to Communicate Mathematical Ideas (1)(D)
What is another representation you could you use to present your solution?
Explain how the representation communicates the same information.

Problem 1 | **Got It?** | **Identifying Common Parts**

a. What is the common side in $\triangle ABD$ and $\triangle DCA$?

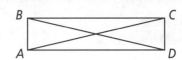

Learning Animation

b. What is the common side in $\triangle ABD$ and $\triangle BAC$?

TEKS Process Standard (1)(E)

Problem 2 | **Got It?** | **Using Common Parts**

Given: $\triangle ACD \cong \triangle BDC$
Prove: $\overline{CE} \cong \overline{DE}$

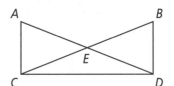

Learning Animation

Lesson 4-7 | Congruence in Overlapping Triangles

160

Problem 3 | **Got It?** | **Using Two Pairs of Triangles**

Given: $\overline{PS} \cong \overline{RS}$, $\angle PSQ \cong \angle RSQ$
Prove: $\triangle QPT \cong \triangle QRT$

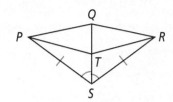

Learning Animation

ELPS Listen as your partner narrates how to write this proof. Ask him or her to rephrase or clarify steps as needed. Then exchange roles and explain how you would write the proof.

TEKS Process Standard (1)(G)

Learning Animation

Problem 4 | **Got It?** | **Separating Overlapping Triangles**

Given: $\angle CAD \cong \angle EAD$, $\angle C \cong \angle E$
Prove: $\overline{BD} \cong \overline{FD}$

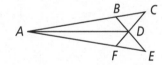

Lesson Check

Do you know HOW?

1. Identify any common sides or angles △DEH and △DFG share.

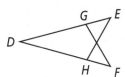

2. In order for $\overline{BC} \cong \overline{DC}$, which two triangles must be congruent?

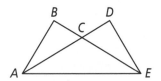

3. In the figure below, $\angle M \cong \angle Q$ and $\angle MNP \cong \angle QPN$. Prove that △NPR is isosceles.

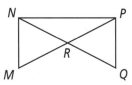

Math Tools

Online Practice

Virtual Nerd Tutorials

 **SOLVE IT!**

Scan page for an interactive
version of this Solve It.

In a video game, two ancient structures shoot light beams toward each other to form a time portal. The portal forms exactly halfway between the two structures. Your character is shown on the grid as a dot. How do you direct your character to the portal? Explain how you found your answer.

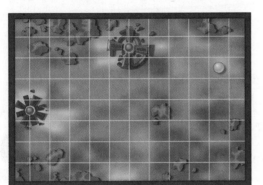

Interactive
Exploration

Vocabulary
Online

 Use Representations to Communicate Mathematical Ideas (1)(E)
Describe how the representation you used to solve the problem successfully organizes and communicates your ideas.

Problem 1 | Got It? | Deriving the Midpoint Formula

Given the midpoint and an endpoint of a segment, can you use the Midpoint Formula to find the other endpoint? Explain.

Learning Animation

Problem 2 | Got It? | Finding the Midpoint

What is the midpoint of $\overline{RS}$ with endpoints $R(5, -10)$ and $S(3, 6)$?

Learning Animation

TEKS Process Standard (1)(C)

Problem 3 | Got It? | Determining the Coordinates of a Point

The endpoints of $\overline{PQ}$ are $(-6, -2)$ and $(3, 4)$. What are the coordinates of a point R on $\overline{PQ}$ that is $\frac{3}{4}$ the distance from P to Q? What technique did you select to solve the problem? Explain your reasoning.

Learning Animation

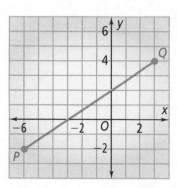

Problem 4 | **Got It?** | Deriving the Distance Formula

Could the formula $PQ = \sqrt{(x_2 - x_1)^2 + (y_2 - y_1)^2}$ also be written as

$PQ = \sqrt{(x_1 - x_2)^2 + (y_1 - y_2)^2}$? Explain your reasoning.

Learning Animation

Problem 5 | **Got It?** | Finding Distance

a. $\overline{SR}$ has endpoints $S(-2, 14)$ and $R(3, -1)$. What is SR to the nearest tenth?

Learning Animation

b. In Problem 5, you found the distance between $U(-7, 5)$ and $V(4, -3)$ is about 13.6. Suppose you let $V(4, -3)$ be (x_1, y_1) and $U(-7, 5)$ be (x_2, y_2). Do you get the same result? Why?

ELPS Read the solution to Problem 5. With a partner, discuss the method used to solve Problem 5. Work together to apply that same method to solve part (a) of the Got It. Read and work through part (b) together.

TEKS Process Standard (1)(E)

Problem 6 | **Got It?** | Finding Distance

Use the zip-line course in Problem 6. Each grid unit represents 5 m. How far do you travel from Platform D to Platform E?

Learning Animation

Lesson 5-1 | Midpoint and Distance in the Coordinate Plane

Lesson Check

Do you know HOW?

1. $\overline{RS}$ has endpoints $R(2, 4)$ and $S(-1, 7)$. What are the coordinates of its midpoint M? What is the distance between R and S? Round to the nearest tenth.

Math Tools

Online Practice

Virtual Nerd Tutorials

2. The midpoint of $\overline{BC}$ is $(5, -2)$. One endpoint is $B(3, 4)$. What are the coordinates of endpoint C?

3. Find the distance d from the point $(2, 5)$ to the origin. How many other points have integer coordinates and are located the same distance d from the origin? How are the coordinates of these points similar?

SOLVE IT!

Interactive Exploration

Vocabulary Online

Cut out a triangle of any shape. Label its largest angle C, and the other angles A and B. Fold A onto C to find the midpoint of $\overline{AC}$. Do the same for $\overline{BC}$. Label the midpoints L and N, and then draw $\overline{LN}$.

Fold the triangle on $\overline{LN}$ as shown.

Fold A to D and fold B to D. Label the vertices M and P as shown. What is the relationship between MP and AB? How do you know? What conjecture can you make about the relationship between LN and AB?

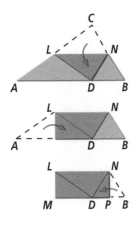

 Explain Mathematical Ideas (1)(G) A classmate questions your solution to the problem. Use precise mathematical language to explain why your solution is correct.

Problem 1 **Got It?** Verifying the Triangle Midsegment Theorem

Verify the Triangle Midsegment Theorem for $\triangle PQR$ with vertices $P(2, 8)$, $Q(4, 0)$, and $R(0, 0)$. Given that S and T are the midpoints of $\overline{RP}$ and $\overline{RQ}$, respectively, show that $\overline{ST} \parallel \overline{PQ}$ and $ST = \frac{1}{2}PQ$.

Learning Animation

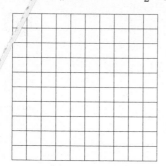

 Problem 2 **Got It?** Identifying Parallel Segments

a. In $\triangle XYZ$, A is the midpoint of $\overline{XY}$, B is the midpoint of $\overline{YZ}$, and C is the midpoint of $\overline{ZX}$. What are the three pairs of parallel segments?

Learning Animation

b. What is $m\angle VUO$ in the figure at the right? Explain your reasoning.

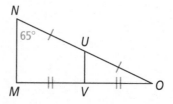

Lesson 5-2 | Midsegments of Triangles

172

Problem 3 **Got It?** Finding Lengths

In the figure below, $AD = 6$ and $DE = 7.5$. What are the lengths of $\overline{DC}$, $\overline{AC}$, $\overline{EF}$, and $\overline{AB}$?

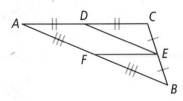

Learning
Animation

 Problem 4 **Got It?** Using a Midsegment of a Triangle

$\overline{CD}$ is a bridge being built over a lake, as shown in the figure. What is the length of the bridge?

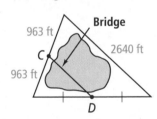

Learning
Animation

ELPS Discuss the meaning of *midsegment* with a partner. Listen to your partner's explanation and ask for more information, if needed. Continue this activity using the vocabulary terms *midpoint*, *distance*, and *length*.

Lesson Check

Do you know HOW?

Use the figure below for Exercises 1 and 2.

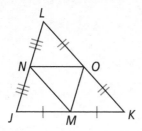

Math
Tools

Online
Practice

Virtual Nerd
Tutorials

1. If $JK = 5x + 20$ and $NO = 20$, what is the value of x?

2. Prove that the four small triangles in the figure are congruent.

3. A surveyor needs to measure the distance PQ across the lake. Beginning at point S, she locates the midpoints of $\overline{SQ}$ and $\overline{SP}$ at M and N. What additional information does the surveyor need to find PQ? How can she use that information?

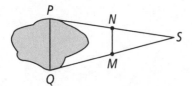

SOLVE IT!

You hang a bulletin board over your desk using string. The bulletin board is crooked. When you straighten the bulletin board, what type of triangle does the string form with the top of the board? How do you know?

Visualize the vertical line along the wall that passed through the nail. What relationships exist between this line and the top edge of the straightened bulletin board? Explain.

Interactive Exploration

Vocabulary Online

Connect Mathematical Ideas (1)(F) What prior knowledge did you draw on to solve the problem?

Problem 1 | **Got It?** | Investigating Perpendicular Bisectors

 Learning Animation

In the construction in Problem 1, $\overleftrightarrow{CD}$ is the perpendicular bisector of $\overline{AB}$. Point M is the midpoint of $\overline{AB}$. How are $\angle CAB$ and $\angle CBA$ related? Explain your reasoning.

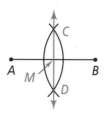

 Problem 2 | **Got It?** | Proving the Perpendicular Bisector Theorem

 Learning Animation

In Problem 2, you used the SAS Postulate to prove the two triangles are congruent. Is it possible to use the SSS Postulate? Explain.

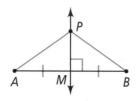

 Problem 3 | **Got It?** | Using the Perpendicular Bisector Theorem

 Learning Animation

What is the length of $\overline{QR}$?

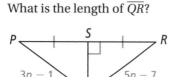

Problem 4 | **Got It?** | **Using a Perpendicular Bisector**

Learning
Animation

Use the diagram in Problem 4.

a. Suppose the director wants the T-shirt stand to be equidistant from the Paddle boats and the Spaceship Shoot. What are the possible locations?

b. Can you place the T-shirt stand so that it is equidistant from the Paddle boats, the Spaceship Shoot, and the Rollin' Coaster? Explain.

ELPS Discuss with a classmate the general method used to solve Problem 4. Together, read part (a) of the Got It aloud. Copy the diagram on paper and apply the process used in Problem 4 to find the locations. Use your diagram to explain to another group how a perpendicular bisector is useful in this context.

TEKS Process Standard (1)(E)

 Problem 5 | **Got It?** | **Using the Angle Bisector Theorem**

Learning
Animation

What is the length of $\overline{FB}$?

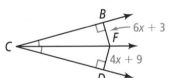

Lesson Check

Do you know HOW?

Use the figure below for Exercises 1–3.

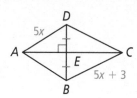

Math
Tools

Online
Practice

Virtual Nerd
Tutorials

1. What is the relationship between $\overline{AC}$ and $\overline{BD}$?

2. Write a compound inequality to express the relationship between *DA*, *DE*, and *DC*. Explain your reasoning.

3. Write a paragraph proof to show $\triangle ADC \cong \triangle ABC$.

SOLVE IT!

Construct a circle and label its center *C*. Choose any three points on the circle and connect them to form a triangle. Draw three lines from *C* such that each line is perpendicular to one side of the triangle. What conjecture can you make about the two segments into which each side of the triangle is divided? Justify your reasoning.

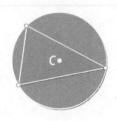

Interactive Exploration

Vocabulary Online

Create Representations to Communicate Mathematical Ideas (1)(E) Describe how the representation you made successfully organizes and communicates your solution to the problem.

Problem 1 Got It? Investigating Bisectors in Triangles

TEKS Process Standard (1)(E)

Learning Animation

Draw one acute triangle and one right triangle. Construct the perpendicular bisector of each side of your triangles. Then make a conjecture about the perpendicular bisectors of the sides of a triangle.

 Problem 2 Got It? Finding the Circumcenter of a Triangle

Learning Animation

What are the coordinates of the circumcenter of the triangle with vertices $A(2, 7)$, $B(10, 7)$, and $C(10, 3)$?

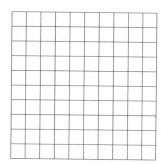

Problem 3 | **Got It?** | **Using a Circumcenter**

Learning
Animation

In Problem 3, the town planner wants to place a bench equidistant from the three trees in the park. Where should he place the bench?

Problem 4 | **Got It?** | **Identifying and Using the Incenter of a Triangle**

Learning
Animation

a. $QN = 5x + 36$ and $QM = 2x + 51$. What is QO?

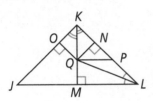

b. Is it possible for QP to equal 50? Explain.

ELPS Work together with a partner to state the Concurrency of Angle Bisectors Theorem in your own words. Use a dictionary in your own language to provide linguistic support for terms such as *concurrent*, *incenter*, and *angle bisector*. Then use the solution method you heard in Problem 4 as a model for solving part (a) of the Got It.

Do you know HOW?

1. What are the coordinates of the circumcenter of the triangle?

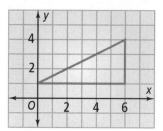

Math
Tools

Online
Practice

Virtual Nerd
Tutorials

2. In the figure, $TV = 3x - 12$ and $TU = 5x - 24$. What is the value of x?

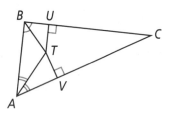

3. Draw a right triangle $\triangle DEF$. Then construct the inscribed circle and the circumscribed circle. Describe your method.

SOLVE IT!

Draw a large acute scalene $\triangle ABC$. On each side, mark the point that is $\frac{1}{5}$ of the distance from one of the side's endpoints, as shown in the diagram. Connect each of these points to the opposite vertex. Repeat this process for $\frac{1}{4}$ and $\frac{1}{3}$. What do you think the result will be for $\frac{1}{2}$? Check your answer. Were you correct?

Interactive Exploration

Vocabulary Online

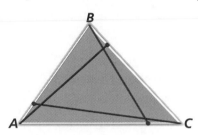

Create Representations to Communicate Mathematical Ideas (1)(E)
Describe how the representation you made successfully organizes and communicates your solution to the problem.

Problem 1 | **Got It?** | **Finding the Length of a Median**

a. In the diagram below, $ZA = 9$. What is the length of $\overline{ZC}$?

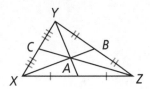

b. What is the ratio of ZA to AC? Explain.

Learning
Animation

TEKS Process Standard (1)(G)

 Problem 2 | **Got It?** | **Identifying Medians and Altitudes**

For $\triangle ABC$, is each segment a *median*, an *altitude*, or *neither*? Explain.

a. $\overline{AD}$

b. $\overline{EG}$

c. $\overline{CF}$

Learning
Animation

Lesson 5-5 | Medians and Altitudes

190

TEKS Process Standard (1)(F)

 Problem 3 **Got It?** Finding the Orthocenter

△*DEF* has vertices *D*(1, 2), *E*(1, 6), and *F*(4, 2). What are the coordinates of the orthocenter of △*DEF*?

Learning Animation

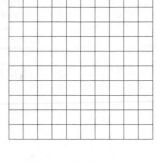

ELPS Read the Got It with a partner. Together, summarize the steps needed to find the coordinates. Be sure to use the appropriate content-based vocabulary such as *altitude*, *horizontal*, *vertical*, and *equation*.

Lesson Check

Do you know HOW?

1. Is $\overline{AP}$ a *median,* an *altitude,* or *neither*? If $AP = 18$, what is KP?

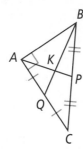

2. Triangle ABC has vertices at $A(-4, 4)$, $B(6, 5)$, and $C(6, 1)$. What are the coordinates of the orthocenter and the centroid of $\triangle ABC$?

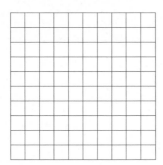

3. Line segment $\overline{BD}$ is both an altitude and a median of $\triangle ABC$. Point F is the orthocenter of $\triangle ABC$. Write a paragraph proof to show $\triangle AFC$ is an isosceles triangle.

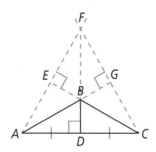

5-6 Indirect Proof

 SOLVE IT!

The goal of this game is to fill in the empty squares with numbers. The numbers 1, 2, 3, and 4 must appear once in each row and once in each column. Complete each game.

Game A

1			2
4		1	
	4		
		2	

Game B

			3
		1	
2		1	
	4		

Interactive Exploration

Vocabulary Online

 Select Techniques to Solve Problems (1)(C) What other techniques could you use to solve the problem? Select one and explain how you would use it.

Problem 1 **Got It?** **Writing the First Step of an Indirect Proof**

Learning
Animation

Suppose you want to write an indirect proof of each statement. As the first step of the proof, what would you assume?

a. △BOX is not acute.

b. At least one pair of shoes you bought cost more than $25.

TEKS Process Standard (1)(D)

 Problem 2 **Got It?** **Identifying Contradictions**

Learning
Animation

a. Which two statements contradict each other?
 I. △XYZ is acute.
 II. △XYZ is scalene.
 III. △XYZ is equiangular.

b. Statements I and II below contradict each other. Statement III is the negation of Statement I. Are Statements II and III equivalent? Explain your reasoning.
 I. △ABC is scalene.
 II. △ABC is equilateral.
 III. △ABC is not scalene.

Problem 3 | **Got It?** | Writing an Indirect Proof

Learning
Animation

Given: $7(x + y) = 70$ and $x \neq 4$

Prove: $y \neq 6$

ELPS Read the Got It with a classmate. Then discuss the approach that should be taken to solve this problem. Once a method has been selected, write out the steps to solve this proof. Use a graphic organizer similar to that featured in Problem 3 as a guide.

Lesson Check

Do you know HOW?

1. Which two statements contradict each other? Explain your answer.
   - I. Points Q, R, and S are collinear.
   - II. $\overline{PS}$ is a median of $\triangle PQR$.
   - III. $RS \neq SQ$

Math
Tools

Online
Practice

Virtual Nerd
Tutorials

2. An indirect proof begins with the following statement. Must the proof show that line a is perpendicular to line b? Explain.

   Assume temporarily that lines a and b are parallel.

3. Write an indirect proof of the following statement. Use the Corresponding Angles Theorem in your proof.

   A triangle may not have two 90° angles.

For a neighborhood improvement project, you volunteer to help build a new sandbox at the town playground. You have two boards that will make up two sides of the triangular sandbox. One is 5 ft long and the other is 8 ft long. Boards come in the lengths shown. Which boards can you use for the third side of the sandbox? Explain.

Interactive Exploration

Vocabulary Online

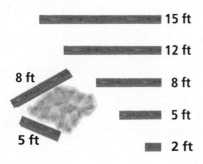

15 ft

12 ft

8 ft

8 ft

8 ft

5 ft

5 ft

2 ft

Analyze Mathematical Relationships (1)(F) What mathematical relationships did you identify in the problem? How did you use them to solve the problem?

Lesson 5-7 | Inequalities in One Triangle

201

Problem 1 **Got It?** **Applying the Corollary**

Why is $m\angle 5 > m\angle C$?

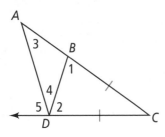

 Problem 2 **Got It?** **Using Theorem 5-10**

Suppose the landscape architect wants to place a drinking fountain at the corner with the second largest angle. Which two streets form the corner with the second-largest angle?

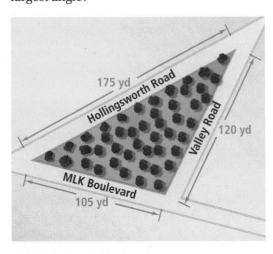

Problem 3 **Got It?** **Using Theorem 5-11**

In the figure, $m\angle S = 24$ and $m\angle O = 130$. Which side of $\triangle SOX$ is the shortest side? Explain your reasoning.

Problem 4 | **Got It?** | Verifying the Triangle Inequality Theorem

Learning Animation

Given: $m\angle A > m\angle B$

Prove: $BC > AC$

 Problem 5 | **Got It?** | Using the Triangle Inequality Theorem

Learning Animation

Can a triangle have sides with the given lengths? Explain.

    a. 2 m, 6 m, and 9 m   **b.** 4 yd, 6 yd, and 9 yd

ELPS Listen as your partner explains the Triangle Inequality Theorem. Ask questions about anything you did not fully understand, and then summarize what you heard. Next, consider how to solve the Got It. Switch roles so your partner listens to your ideas for solving the problem, then summarizes them.

 Problem 6 | **Got It?** | Finding Possible Side Lengths

Learning Animation

A triangle has side lengths of 4 in. and 7 in. What is the range of possible lengths for the third side?

 Lesson Check

Do you know HOW?

1. For $\triangle ABC$, which side is the longest? Which angle is the smallest? Explain your answers.

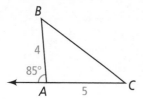

2. If m is a positive real number, can a triangle have sides of lengths m, $4m + 2$, and $3m + 1$? Explain.

3. Two sides of a triangle have lengths k and $2k$. Find the range of possible lengths for the third side in terms of k.

SOLVE IT!

Think of a clock or watch that has an hour hand and a minute hand. As minutes pass, the distance between the tip of the hour hand and the tip of the minute hand changes. The distance is x in the figure below. What is the order of the times below from least to greatest length of x? How do you know?

1:00, 3:00, 5:00, 8:30, 1:30, 12:20

Interactive Exploration

Vocabulary Online

Evaluate Reasonableness (1)(B) Explain how you know your solution is reasonable.

Problem 1 **Got It?** **Using the Hinge Theorem**

a. What inequality relates LN and OQ in the figure?

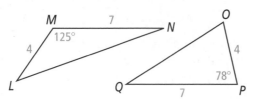

Learning
Animation

b. In $\triangle ABC$, $AB = 3$, $BC = 4$, and $CA = 6$. In $\triangle PQR$, $PQ = 3$, $QR = 5$, and $RP = 6$. How can you use indirect reasoning to explain why $m\angle P > m\angle A$?

TEKS Process Standard (1)(A)

Problem 2 **Got It?** **Applying the Hinge Theorem**

The diagram below shows a pair of scissors in two different positions. In which position is the distance between the tips of the two blades greater? Use the Hinge Theorem to justify your answer.

Learning
Animation

ELPS Take turns reading the Got It aloud with a partner. Briefly discuss the Hinge Theorem as explained in Problem 2. Use the Hinge Theorem and the images of the scissors to answer the question.

TEKS Process Standard (1)(F)

 Problem 3 | **Got It?** | Using the Converse of the Hinge Theorem

Learning
Animation

What is the range of possible values for *x* in the figure below?

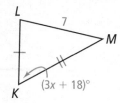

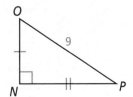

 Problem 4 | **Got It?** | Proving Relationships in Triangles

Learning
Animation

Given: $m\angle MON = 80$, O is the midpoint of $\overline{LN}$

Prove: $LM > MN$

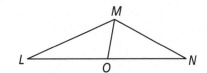

Do you know HOW?

1. Write an inequality relating *FD* and *BC*.

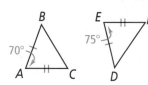

2. Find the range of possible values for *y*.

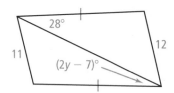

3. In the figure below, $\overline{AB} \cong \overline{BX} \cong \overline{XC}$ and $m\angle ABX < m\angle BXC$. Use the Hinge Theorem to write an inequality that relates *AX* and *BC*. If $AX = 5z - 9$ and $BC = 3z - 1$, what is one possible value of *z*?

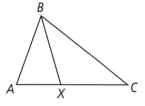

Lesson 5-8 | Inequalities in Two Triangles

210

SOLVE IT!

Sketch a convex pentagon, hexagon, and heptagon. For each figure, draw all the diagonals you can from one vertex. What conjecture can you make about the relationship between the number of sides of a polygon and the number of triangles formed by the diagonals from one vertex?

Interactive Exploration

Vocabulary Online

 Analyze Mathematical Relationships (1)(F) What mathematical relationships did you identify in the problem? How did you use them to solve the problem?

TEKS Process Standard (1)(C)

Problem 1 | Got It? | Investigating Interior Angles of Polygons

What is the sum of the measures of the interior angles of an octagon? Use your conjecture from Problem 1.

Learning Animation

Problem 2 | Got It? | Finding a Polygon Angle Sum

a. What is the sum of the interior angle measures of a 17-gon?

b. The sum of the interior angle measures of a polygon is 1980. How can you find the number of sides in the polygon?

Learning Animation

Problem 3 | Got It? | Using the Polygon Angle-Sum Theorem

What is the measure of each interior angle in a regular nonagon?

Learning Animation

ELPS Read the Got It aloud. What parts of the word *nonagon* do you recognize that may help you describe it? Discuss the meaning with the class. Solve the problem, then exchange papers and read your partner's answer.

Problem 4 | Got It? | Using the Polygon Angle-Sum Theorem

Learning Animation

What is $m\angle G$ in quadrilateral *EFGH*?

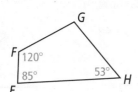

Problem 5 | Got It? | Investigating Exterior Angles of Polygons

Learning Animation

Draw a hexagon. Then draw an exterior angle at each vertex of the hexagon. Choose from a variety of tools (such as a ruler, a protractor, or a graphing calculator) to investigate the exterior angles. Explain your choice. Observe any patterns. Do your observations support your conjecture in Problem 5? Explain.

TEKS Process Standard (1)(F)

Problem 6 | Got It? | Finding an Exterior Angle Measure

Learning Animation

What is the measure of an exterior angle of a regular nonagon?

Lesson 6-1 | The Polygon Angle-Sum Theorems

215

Lesson Check

Do you know HOW?

1. What is the sum of the interior angle measures of an 11-gon? What is the sum of the exterior angle measures?

Math Tools

Online Practice

Virtual Nerd Tutorials

2. A regular polygon has interior angles that each measure 144. How many sides does the polygon have?

3. A jewelry designer makes a pendant for a necklace using regular pentagon *ABCDE* and angle bisectors $\overline{CF}$ and $\overline{DG}$. She needs to know if $\angle E \cong \angle DHF$. Explain whether she can make this conclusion and, if so, why.

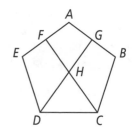

SOLVE IT!

Scan page for an interactive version of this Solve It.

Which triangles are congruent? How do you know?

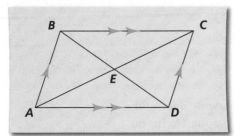

Interactive Exploration

Vocabulary Online

 Connect Mathematical Ideas (1)(F) What prior knowledge did you draw on to solve the problem?

Problem 1 | Got It? | **Using Consecutive Angles**

Suppose you adjust the lamp in Problem 1 so that $m\angle S = 86$.
What is $m\angle R$ in $\square PQRS$?

 Read the Got It and point out the *consecutive angles, opposite sides,* and *supplementary angles* in the diagram. How does visual support help you understand these terms? Which of these angles will help you solve the Got It?

TEKS Process Standard (1)(G)

Problem 2 | Got It? | **Using Properties of Parallelograms in a Proof**

Given: $\square ABCD$, $\overline{AK} \cong \overline{MK}$

Prove: $\angle BCD \cong \angle CMD$

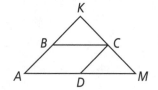

Problem 3 | Got It? | **Using Algebra to Find Lengths**

Learning
Animation

a. Find the values of x and y in $\square PQRS$. What are PR and SQ?

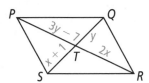

b. In part (a), does it matter which variable you solve for first? Explain.

TEKS Process Standard (1)(F)

Problem 4 | Got It? | **Using Parallel Lines and Transversals**

Learning
Animation

Use the figure below. If $EF = FG = GH = 6$ and $AD = 15$, what is CD?

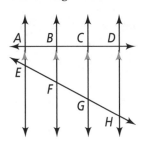

Lesson Check

Do you know HOW?

1. Find $m\angle A$, $m\angle D$, and AB.

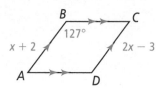

Math Tools

Online Practice

Virtual Nerd Tutorials

2. A parallelogram has an angle whose measure is 4 times the measure of another angle of the parallelogram. What are the measures of the angles of the parallelogram?

3. The director of a marching band uses a coordinate plane to plan the band's shows. During the half-time show at a football game, the four tuba players will form $\square JKLM$. The coordinates of three tuba players are shown. What are the coordinates of the fourth tuba player?

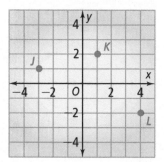

6-3 Proving That a Quadrilateral Is a Parallelogram

SOLVE IT!

Each section of glass in the exterior of a building in Macau, China, forms an equilateral triangle. Do you think the window washer's feet stay parallel to the ground as he lands at each level of windows? Explain. (Assume that the bases of the lowest triangles are parallel to the ground.)

Interactive Exploration

Vocabulary Online

Use Representations to Communicate Mathematical Ideas (1)(E) Describe how the representation you used to solve the problem successfully organizes and communicates your ideas.

Problem 1 **Got It?** Proving Theorem 6-8

Learning
Animation

In Problem 1, you proved Theorem 6-8. Use one of the theorems in this lesson to complete the following proof.

Given: $\angle S \cong \angle U$, $\angle STV \cong \angle UVT$

Prove: $STUV$ is a parallelogram.

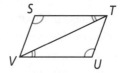

TEKS Process Standard (1)(G)

 Problem 2 **Got It?** Proving Theorem 6-10

Learning
Animation

Given: $\angle J \cong \angle NKL$, $\angle MLK \cong \angle NKL$,
$\angle M \cong \angle KLP$, $\angle JKL \cong \angle KLP$

Prove: $JKLM$ is a parallelogram.

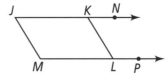

Problem 3 | Got It? | Proving Theorem 6-11

Learning Animation

In Problem 3, you proved Theorem 6-11. Use one of the theorems in this lesson to complete the following proof.

Given: $\overline{TQ} \cong \overline{RS}$, $\angle TQX \cong \angle RSX$

Prove: $QRST$ is a parallelogram.

Problem 4 | Got It? | Finding Values for Parallelograms

Learning Animation

a. For what values of x and y must $EFGH$ be a parallelogram?

$$(3y - 2)°$$
$$(4x + 13)°$$
$$(y + 10)°$$
$$(12x + 7)°$$

b. For what values of m and n must $PQRS$ be a parallelogram?

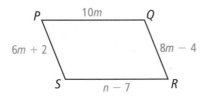

$10m$

$6m + 2$

$8m - 4$

$n - 7$

Problem 5 | **Got It?** | **Deciding Whether a Quadrilateral Is a Parallelogram**

Learning Animation

Can you prove that the quadrilateral is a parallelogram based on the given information? Explain.

a. Given: $m\angle E = m\angle G = 72, m\angle F = 107$

Prove: *DEFG* is a parallelogram.

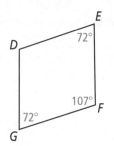

b. Given: $UY = WY = 4, UV = WX = 5$

Prove: *UVWX* is a parallelogram.

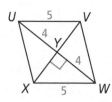

c. Given: $\overline{QR} \cong \overline{RS} \cong \overline{ST} \cong \overline{TQ}$

Prove: *QRST* is a parallelogram.

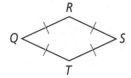

d. Given: $MJ = KL = 7, \angle JMK \cong \angle LKM$

Prove: *JKLM* is a parallelogram.

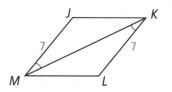

Problem 6 | Got It? | Identifying Parallelograms

A truck sits on the platform of a vehicle lift. Two moving arms raise the platform until a mechanic can fit underneath. What is the maximum height that the vehicle lift can elevate the truck? Explain.

Learning Animation

ELPS Study the illustration both before and after you read Problem 6. Then reread Theorem 6-8 and solve the problem. Use the terms *congruent angles, congruent sides, parallelogram,* and *opposite sides* in your explanation. Draw additional illustrations as you work through the problem.

Do you know HOW?

1. For what value of *y* must *LMNP* be a parallelogram?

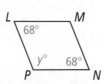

Math Tools

Online Practice

Virtual Nerd Tutorials

2. In the figure, *B* is the midpoint of $\overline{AD}$, and *C* is the midpoint of $\overline{AE}$. For what value of *x* must *AFCB* be a parallelogram?

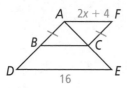

3. A truss is a structure made of beams that form triangles. The figure shows part of the plan for a truss bridge. What measure of ∠1 ensures that quadrilateral *PQRS* is a parallelogram? Explain.

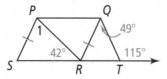

PearsonTEXAS.com

Fold a piece of notebook paper in half. Fold it in half again in the other direction. Draw a diagonal line from one vertex to the other. Cut through the folded paper along that line. Unfold the paper. What do you notice about the sides and about the diagonals of the figure you formed?

Interactive Exploration

Vocabulary Online

Create Representations to Communicate Mathematical Ideas (1)(E)
Describe how the representation you made successfully organizes and communicates your solution to the problem.

Problem 1 | **Got It?** | **Classifying Special Parallelograms**

Learning
Animation

Use the figure in Problem 1. Is □*EFGH* a rhombus, a rectangle, or a square? Explain.

 Discuss with a classmate. Compare a rhombus, a rectangle, and a square. What do they have in common? How do they differ? Make a Venn diagram to show the relationships among these parallelograms.

TEKS Process Standard (1)(C)

 Problem 2 | **Got It?** | **Investigating Diagonals of Quadrilaterals**

Learning
Animation

a. Choose from a variety of tools (such as a protractor, a ruler, a compass, or a geoboard) to investigate patterns in the diagonals of squares. Explain your choice.

b. Make several squares. Then make a conjecture about the diagonals of squares.

TEKS Process Standard (1)(F)

Problem 3 | **Got It?** | **Finding Angle Measures**

What are the measures of the numbered angles in rhombus *PQRS*?

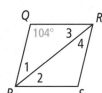

Learning Animation

Problem 4 | **Got It?** | **Finding Diagonal Length**

a. If $LN = 4x - 17$ and $MO = 2x + 13$, what are the lengths of the diagonals of rectangle *LMNO*?

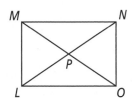

Learning Animation

b. What type of triangle is △*PMN*? Explain.

Lesson Check

Do you know HOW?

1. What are the measures of the numbered angles in the rhombus?

Math Tools

Online Practice

Virtual Nerd Tutorials

2. *JKLM* is a rectangle. If $JL = 4x - 12$ and $MK = x$, what is the value of x? What is the length of each diagonal?

3. A set designer prepares a plan for a backdrop in a play, as shown. According to the plan, *ABCD* is a rectangle and $\overline{DF} \cong \overline{CE}$. Can the set designer conclude that $\triangle ADE \cong \triangle BCF$? Explain.

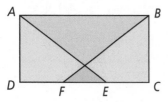

SOLVE IT!

Which vertices form a square? A rhombus? A rectangle? Justify your answers.

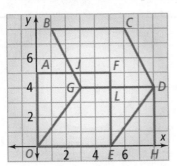

Interactive Exploration

Vocabulary Online

 Select Techniques to Solve Problems (1)(C) What other techniques could you use to solve the problem? Select one and explain how you would use it.

TEKS Process Standard (1)(G)

 Problem 1 | **Got It?** | Proving Theorem 6-16

Learning
Animation

In Problem 1, how did you use the fact that *ABCD* is a parallelogram to prove that it is a rhombus? Explain.

 Problem 2 | **Got It?** | Proving Theorem 6-19

Learning
Animation

Why is showing that the diagonals of a quadrilateral are perpendicular bisectors not sufficient to prove the quadrilateral is a square?

TEKS Process Standard (1)(F)

 Problem 3 | **Got It?** | Identifying Rhombuses, Rectangles, and Squares

Learning
Animation

The diagonals of a quadrilateral are congruent. Can you conclude that the quadrilateral is a rectangle? Explain.

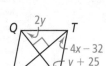 **Problem 4** | **Got It?** | Using Properties of Special Parallelograms

For what values of x and y is quadrilateral $QRST$ a rhombus?

Learning Animation

Q 2y T
4x − 32
y + 25
R 2x + 4 S

ELPS Take turns reading the question aloud. Discuss what the question is asking. Rephrase the question using a more familiar word order. Write out an equation to use as you solve the problem together.

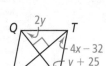 **Problem 5** | **Got It?** | Using Properties of Parallelograms

In Problem 5, is there only one rectangle that can be formed by pulling the ropes taut? Explain.

Learning Animation

Lesson 6-5 | Conditions for Rhombuses, Rectangles, and Squares

241

Lesson Check

Do you know HOW?

1. Can you conclude that the parallelogram is a rhombus, a rectangle, or a square? Explain.

a.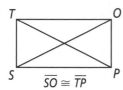
$\overline{SO} \cong \overline{TP}$

b.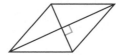

2. In quadrilateral $ABCD$, $m\angle ABC = 56$. What values of $m\angle 2$, $m\angle 3$, and $m\angle 4$ ensure that quadrilateral $ABCD$ is a rhombus?

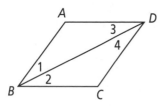

3. A square has opposite vertices $(-2, 1)$ and $(2, 3)$. What are the other two vertices? Explain.

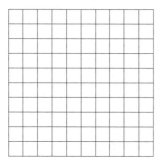

Two isosceles triangles form the figure below. Each white segment is a midsegment of a triangle. What can you determine about the angles in region 2? In region 3? Explain.

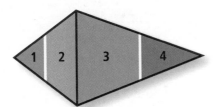

Interactive Exploration

Vocabulary Online

 Explain Mathematical Ideas (1)(G) A classmate questions your solution to the problem. Use precise mathematical language to explain why your solution is correct.

TEKS Process Standard (1)(F)

 Problem 1 **Got It?** **Finding Angle Measures in Trapezoids**

Learning Animation

a. In the diagram, *PQRS* is an isosceles trapezoid and $m\angle R = 106$. What are $m\angle P$, $m\angle Q$, and $m\angle S$?

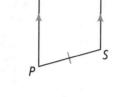

b. In Problem 1, if *CDEF* were not an isosceles trapezoid, would $\angle C$ and $\angle D$ still be supplementary? Explain.

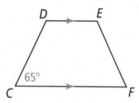

 Problem 2 **Got It?** **Finding Angle Measures in Isosceles Trapezoids**

Learning Animation

A fan like the one in Problem 2 has 15 congruent angles meeting at the center. What are the measures of the base angles of the trapezoids in its second ring?

Problem 3 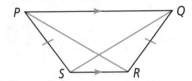 **Got It?** **Investigating the Diagonals of Isosceles Trapezoids**

Learning Animation

Choose from a variety of tools (such as a protractor, a ruler, or a compass) to investigate patterns in the diagonals of isosceles trapezoid *PQRS*. Explain your choice. Do your observations support your conjecture in Problem 3? Explain your reasoning.

 Problem 4 **Got It?** **Using the Midsegment of a Trapezoid**

Learning Animation

a. $\overline{MN}$ is the midsegment of trapezoid *PQRS*. What is *x*? What is *MN*?

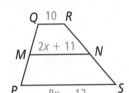

b. How many midsegments can a triangle have? How many midsegments can a trapezoid have? Explain.

ELPS Explain the Trapezoid Midsegment Theorem to a classmate. Point to a diagram as you speak. Help your partner better understand what you mean by describing terms if you do not know the formal vocabulary. Solve the Got It together.

 Problem 5 **Got It?** **Finding Angle Measures in Kites**

Learning Animation

Quadrilateral *KLMN* is a kite. What are $m\angle 1$, $m\angle 2$, and $m\angle 3$?

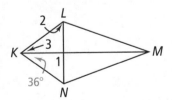

Lesson Check

Do you know HOW?

1. What are the measures of the numbered angles?

a.
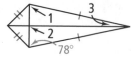

b.
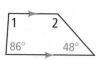

Math Tools

Online Practice

Virtual Nerd Tutorials

2. Quadrilateral *WXYZ* is an isosceles trapezoid. Are the two trapezoids formed by drawing midsegment $\overline{QR}$ isosceles trapezoids? Explain.

3. Find the length of the perimeter of trapezoid *LMNP* with midsegment $\overline{QR}$.

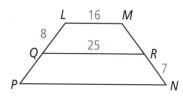

Lesson 6-6 | Trapezoids and Kites

248

You and a friend are playing a board game. Players place rubber bands on their own square grid to form different shapes. The object of the game is to guess the vertices of your opponent's shape. How would you place pieces on the grid shown to complete a right isosceles triangle? Sketch the triangle and justify the placement of each piece.

Interactive Exploration

Vocabulary Online

Connect Mathematical Ideas (1)(F) What prior knowledge did you draw on to solve the problem?

Problem 1 | **Got It?** | **Classifying a Triangle**

△*DEF* has vertices *D*(0, 0), *E*(1, 4), and *F*(5, 2). Is △*DEF* *scalene, isosceles,* or *equilateral*?

Learning Animation

 Problem 2 | **Got It?** | **Classifying a Quadrilateral**

▱*MNPQ* has vertices *M*(0, 1), *N*(−1, 4), *P*(2, 5), and *Q*(3, 2).

a. Is ▱*MNPQ* a rectangle? Explain.

Learning Animation

b. Is ▱*MNPQ* a square? Explain.

c. The triangle in Problem 1 is shown at the right. Is the triangle a right triangle? Explain.

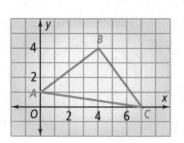

Lesson 7-1 | **Polygons in the Coordinate Plane**

Problem 3 Got It? Verifying Parallelism of Line Segments

Learning Animation

In Problem 2, you proved that ▱*ABCD* is a rhombus by showing that the diagonals are perpendicular. In what other way could you prove that ▱*ABCD* is a rhombus? Compare the two strategies.

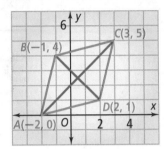

 Discuss with your classmates the ways you would verify that a shape is a rhombus. Work together to make a poster that explains how to determine whether the diagonals are perpendicular or whether opposite sides are congruent.

 Problem 4 Got It? Verifying Congruence of Segments

Learning Animation

In Problem 4, you proved △*DEF* is an isosceles triangle without using the Distance Formula. Use the Distance Formula to confirm △*DEF* is an isosceles triangle. Compare the two approaches.

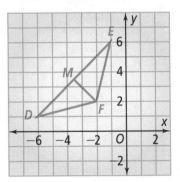

Lesson Check

Do you know HOW?

1. Quadrilateral *QRST* is a parallelogram. Can *QRST* be classified more precisely? Explain your reasoning.

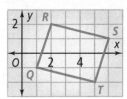

2. $\triangle TRI$ has vertices $T(-3, 4)$, $R(a, 4)$, and $I(0, 0)$. If $\triangle TRI$ is an isosceles triangle with $\overline{TI} \cong \overline{RI}$, what is the value of a? Explain.

3. Quadrilateral *ABCD* has vertices $A(-7, 2)$, $B(-1, 6)$, $C(3, 0)$, and $D(-3, -4)$. Quadrilateral *EFGH* is formed by connecting the midpoints of *ABCD*. What is the most precise classification of *EFGH*? Use opposite sides and angles to prove your classification is correct.

Lesson Check

Do you UNDERSTAND?

4. Justify Mathematical Arguments (1)(G) If you can verify perpendicularity for the diagonals of a parallelogram, what does this tell you about the parallelogram? Justify your answer.

5. Use Representations to Communicate Mathematical Ideas (1)(E) Describe how you would determine whether the lengths of the medians from base angles *D* and *F* are congruent.

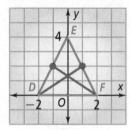

6. Explain Mathematical Ideas (1)(G) A student says that the quadrilateral with vertices $D(1, 2)$, $E(0, 7)$, $F(5, 6)$, and $G(7, 0)$ is a rhombus because its diagonals are perpendicular. Do you agree with the student? Explain using precise mathematical language.

TEXAS Test Practice

Multiple Choice

For Exercises 1–4, choose the correct letter.

1. Which of the following best describes the relationship between the triangle at the right and the triangle with vertices $D(-2, 1)$, $E(-1, -3)$, and $F(4, 0)$?

   A. The two triangles are congruent because of the SSS Postulate.

   B. The two triangles are congruent because they are both scalene.

   C. The two triangles are not congruent because one is scalene and one is isosceles.

   D. The two triangles cannot be congruent because $\overline{AB}$ is not congruent to $\overline{DE}$.

2. What is the most accurate description of the polygon at the right?

   F. rhombus

   G. square

   H. rectangle

   J. parallelogram

   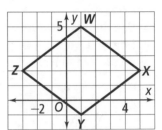

3. What is the most accurate description of the polygon at the right?

   A. rhombus

   B. trapezoid

   C. kite

   D. quadrilateral

   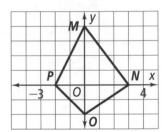

4. A quadrilateral has opposite sides with the same slopes and consecutive sides with slopes that are reciprocals. What is the most precise classification of the quadrilateral?

   F. quadrilateral   **H.** rectangle

   G. parallelogram   **J.** trapezoid

Short Response

5. What type of quadrilateral is formed by connecting the points $(0, 9)$, $(3, 6)$, $(0, 1)$, and $(-3, 6)$? Explain.

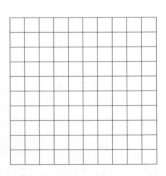

Lesson 7-1 | Polygons in the Coordinate Plane

256

Scan page for an interactive
version of this Solve It.

The points shown on the graph are three vertices of a parallelogram. Point *D* is the
fourth vertex. What are the coordinates for one possible location of *D*? How do you
know? How many others can you find?

Interactive
Exploration

Vocabulary
Online

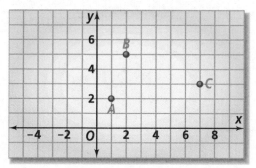

Evaluate Reasonableness (1)(B) Explain how you know your solution
is reasonable.

Problem 1 | **Got It?** | **Naming Coordinates**

What are the coordinates of the vertices of each figure?

a. *RECT* is a rectangle with height *a* and length *2b*. The *y*-axis bisects $\overline{EC}$ and $\overline{RT}$.

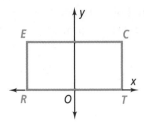

b. *KITE* is a kite where $IE = 2a$, $KO = b$, and $OT = c$. The *x*-axis bisects $\overline{IE}$.

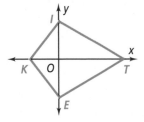

Lesson 7-2 | **Applying Coordinate Geometry**

258

TEKS Process Standard (1)(F)

Problem 2 | **Got It?** | **Using Variable Coordinates**

a. The figure from Problem 2 is shown below. Explain why the *x*-coordinate of *B* is the sum of 2*a* and 2*b*.

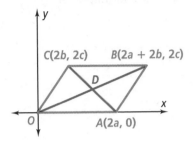

b. The diagram below shows a trapezoid with the base centered at the origin. Is the trapezoid isosceles? Explain.

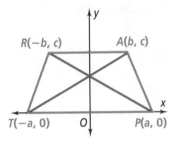

 ELPS Discuss with a classmate the new expression *using variable coordinates* heard during today's class instruction and interaction. Explain your understanding of this expression. Solve the Got It together, using this expression when applicable.

TEKS Process Standard (1)(D)

Problem 3 | **Got It?** | **Planning a Coordinate Proof**

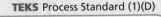

Plan a coordinate proof of the Trapezoid Midsegment Theorem (Theorem 6-22), which states if a quadrilateral is a trapezoid, then

(1) the midsegment is parallel to the bases, and

(2) the length of the midsegment is half the sum of the lengths of the bases.

Lesson Check

Do you know HOW?

1. Isosceles trapezoid *PQRS* has height 2*c* and the *x*-axis as its midsegment. The *y*-axis bisects $\overline{PQ}$ and $\overline{RS}$. If *PQ* = 2*a* and *SR* = 2*b*, what are the coordinates of vertices *P*, *Q*, *R*, and *S*?

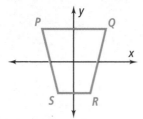

Math Tools

Online Practice

Virtual Nerd Tutorials

2. In parallelogram *KLMO*, *OM* = 2*a*. Without using any new variables, write expressions for the slopes of the diagonals of *KLMO*.

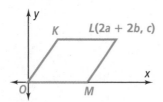

3. a. Draw a square whose diagonals of length 2*b* lie on the *x*- and *y*-axes. Give the coordinates of the vertices of the square. Compute the length of a side of the square.

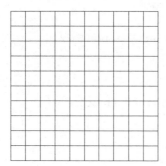

b. Find the slopes of two adjacent sides of the square. Do the slopes show that the sides are perpendicular? Explain.

Lesson Check

Do you UNDERSTAND?

Math Tools

Online Practice

Virtual Nerd Tutorials

4. **Select Techniques to Solve Problems (1)(C)** How does using variable coordinates help to generalize figures in the coordinate plane?

5. **Analyze Mathematical Relationships (1)(F)** A vertex of a quadrilateral has coordinates (a, b). The x-coordinates of the other three vertices are a or $-a$, and the y-coordinates are b or $-b$. What kind of quadrilateral is the figure?

6. **Explain Mathematical Ideas (1)(G)** A classmate says the endpoints of the midsegment of the trapezoid below are $\left(\frac{b}{2}, \frac{c}{2}\right)$ and $\left(\frac{d+a}{2}, \frac{c}{2}\right)$. Do you agree with your classmate? Explain using precise mathematical language.

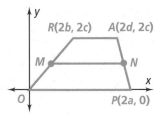

TEXAS Test Practice

Multiple Choice

For Exercises 1–5, choose the correct letter.

1. The locations of a restaurant, elementary school, car wash, and temple are represented by rectangle *RECT* as shown. What are the coordinates of the elementary school, point *E*?

   A. $(2a, d)$

   B. $(a, 2d)$

   C. $(-2a, d)$

   D. $(2a, 2d)$

   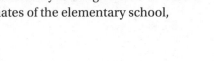

2. Isosceles trapezoid *TRAP* is shown at the right. What are the coordinates of the midpoint of *TP*?

   F. $\left(\frac{-7a}{2}, \frac{-b}{2}\right)$

   G. $\left(\frac{-3a-b}{2}, \frac{-b}{2}\right)$

   H. $\left(\frac{-3a}{2}, \frac{-4a-b}{2}\right)$

   J. $\left(\frac{a}{2}, \frac{b}{2}\right)$

   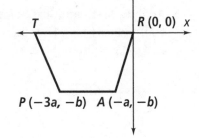

3. What type of triangle is shown at the right?

   A. equilateral   **C.** isosceles

   B. right   **D.** scalene

   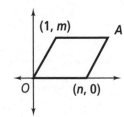

4. What is the most precise description of a quadrilateral with coordinates $A(-a, b)$, $B(3a, b)$, $C(3a, -b)$, $D(-a, -b)$?

   F. kite   **H.** rhombus

   G. rectangle   **J.** square

5. Given the parallelogram at the right, what coordinates for point *A* can you write without using any new variables?

   A. (n, m) **C.** $(n + m, 1)$

   B. $(1 + n, m)$ **D.** $(m, n + 1)$

   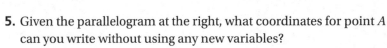

Short Response

6. What type of quadrilateral is formed by connecting the points $(0, 0)$, $(3x, b)$, $(18x, b)$, and $(15x, 0)$? Explain.

SOLVE IT!

The coordinates of three vertices of a rectangle are $(-2a, 0)$, $(2a, 0)$, and $(2a, 2b)$. A diagonal joins one of these points with the fourth vertex. What are the coordinates of the midpoint of the diagonal? Justify your answer.

Interactive Exploration

Vocabulary Online

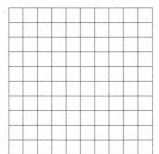

 Create Representations to Communicate Mathematical Ideas (1)(E)
Describe how the representation you made successfully organizes and communicates your solution to the problem.

Problem 1 | **Got It?** | **Proving Congruence of Medians**

What is the advantage of using coordinates $P(-2a, 0)$, $Q(0, 2b)$, and $R(2a, 0)$ rather than $P(-a, 0)$, $Q(0, b)$, and $R(a, 0)$?

Learning Animation

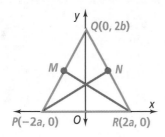

Problem 2 | **Got It?** | **Proving the Triangle Midsegment Theorem**

In Problem 2, you wrote a coordinate proof of the Triangle Midsegment Theorem.

Use coordinate geometry to prove the Trapezoid Midsegment Theorem (Theorem 6-22).

Given: $\overline{MN}$ is the midsegment of trapezoid *ORAP*.

Prove: $\overline{MN} \parallel \overline{OP}$, $\overline{MN} \parallel \overline{RA}$, $MN = \frac{1}{2}(OP + RA)$

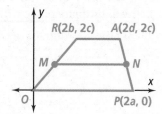

Learning Animation

ELPS Discuss with a classmate the steps you will need to take to complete this proof. Seek clarification by asking your partner to rephrase steps you do not fully understand. Then use the agreed-upon steps to complete the Got It.

Lesson Check

Do you know HOW?

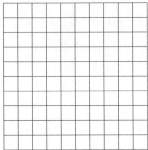
For Exercises 1 and 2, use coordinate geometry to prove that the diagonals of a rectangle are congruent.

1. **a.** Place rectangle *PQRS*, with height *b* and width *a*, in the coordinate plane with *P* at $(0, 0)$.

   b. What are the coordinates of *Q*, *R*, and *S*?

   c. Write the *Given* and *Prove* statements.

2. Write a coordinate proof.

3. Write a coordinate proof to show that the midpoints of the sides of an isosceles triangle form another isosceles triangle. Use the figure shown.

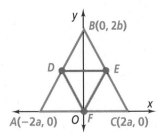

Lesson 7-3 | Proofs Using Coordinate Geometry

Do you UNDERSTAND?

Math
Tools

Online
Practice

Virtual Nerd
Tutorials

4. Select Techniques to Solve Problems (1)(C) The Slope Formula, the Midpoint Formula, and the Distance Formula are important when writing coordinate proofs. Give an example of how each formula could be used.

5. Create Representations to Communicate Mathematical Ideas (1)(E) Describe a good strategy for placing the vertices of a rhombus for a coordinate proof.

6. Explain Mathematical Ideas (1)(G) Your classmate places a trapezoid on the coordinate plane. What is the error?

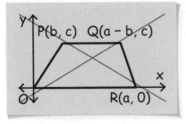

Multiple Choice

For Exercises 1–4, choose the correct letter.

For Exercises 1 and 2, use the diagram at the right.

1. Which of the following could you use as a first step to prove that quadrilateral *TRAP* is an isosceles trapezoid?

   A. Prove $AP = \frac{1}{2} TR$.

   B. Prove $\overline{RA} \perp \overline{AP}$.

   C. Prove $\overline{TR} \parallel \overline{PA}$.

   D. Prove that there are no right angles formed by the line segments.

2. Which of the following could you use as a second step to prove *TRAP* is an isosceles trapezoid?

   F. Prove $RA = TP$.

   G. Prove $\overline{RA} \parallel \overline{TP}$.

   H. Prove $\angle R \cong \angle P$.

   J. It is impossible to prove *TRAP* is an isosceles trapezoid because you cannot prove $\angle R \cong \angle T$ using coordinate geometry.

3. Which formula or formulas do you need to use to prove that if the segments connecting the midpoints of a trapezoid are joined they form a parallelogram?

   A. Slope Formula

   B. Distance Formula

   C. Distance Formula and Slope Formula

   D. Slope Formula and Midpoint Formula

4. Which formula or formulas do you need to use to prove that a quadrilateral is an isosceles trapezoid?

   F. Slope Formula

   G. Distance Formula

   H. Distance Formula and Slope Formula

   J. Slope Formula and Midpoint Formula

Short Response

5. How would you use coordinate geometry to prove that two line segments are perpendicular?

SOLVE IT!

Suppose you write the letters shown on squares of tracing paper so their shapes are visible from both sides. For each pair of words, how can you move the squares of paper to change Word A into Word B? Note: No square should remain in its original position.

Interactive Exploration

Vocabulary Online

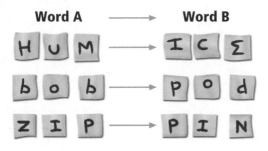

Word A ⟶ **Word B**

Use Multiple Representations to Communicate Mathematical Ideas (1)(D)
What is another representation you could use to present your solution? Explain how the representation communicates the same information.

Problem 1 | **Got It?** | **Identifying a Rigid Transformation**

Does the transformation appear to be a rigid transformation? Explain.

Learning
Animation

a.

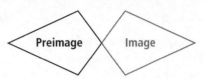

b.

 Discuss with a classmate the meanings of the terms *rigid* and *transformation*. What prior knowledge do you have with these words, and how will this information help you identify a *rigid transformation*?

TEKS Process Standard (1)(F)

Problem 2 | **Got It?** | **Naming Images and Corresponding Parts**

In the diagram, $\triangle NID \rightarrow \triangle SUP$.

a. What are the images of $\angle I$ and point D?

b. What are the pairs of corresponding sides?

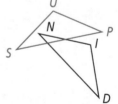

Learning
Animation

Lesson 8-1 | Translations

270

Problem 3 | **Got It?** | Finding the Image of a Translation

a. What are the vertices of $T_{\langle 1, -4 \rangle}(\triangle ABC)$? Copy $\triangle ABC$ and graph its image.

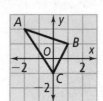

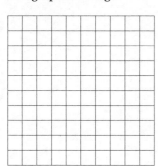

b. In your graph above, draw $\overline{AA'}$, $\overline{BB'}$, and $\overline{CC'}$. What relationships exist among these three segments? How do you know?

Learning Animation

TEKS Process Standard (1)(D)

Problem 4 | **Got It?** | Writing a Rule to Describe a Translation

The translation image of $\triangle LMN$ is $\triangle L'M'N'$ with $L'(1, -2)$, $M'(3, -4)$, and $N'(6, -2)$. What is a coordinate rule that describes the translation?

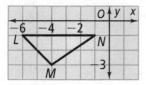

Learning Animation

Problem 5 | **Got It?** | Composing Translations

Use the figure in Problem 5. The bishop next moves 3 squares left and 3 squares down. Where is the bishop in relation to its original position?

Learning Animation

Lesson 8-1 | Translations

271

Do you know HOW?

1. Graph $T_{<-3, -4>}(NILE)$.

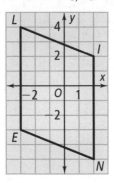

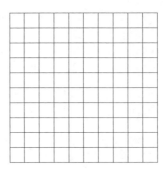

Math
Tools

Online
Practice

Virtual Nerd
Tutorials

2. $\triangle ABC$ has coordinates $A(-4, 1)$, $B(-3, -2)$, and $C(1, -1)$. A translation maps $\triangle ABC$ to $\triangle A'B'C'$ with coordinate $A'(1, -2)$. What are the coordinates of B' and C'?

3. The following combination of translations map quadrilateral $FGHJ$ to $F'G'H'J'$. Write a rule for a single translation that maps $FGHJ$ to $F'G'H'J'$.

$T_{<-1, 4>}(x, y)$, followed by $T_{<3, 2>}(x, y)$, followed by $T_{<-4, -5>}(x, y)$

SOLVE IT!

Scan page for an interactive
version of this Solve It.

Look at the shapes on the grid. Visualize flipping each shape across its dashed line. What word do the images of the shapes form? Sketch the results of flipping all the shapes.

Interactive
Exploration

Vocabulary
Online

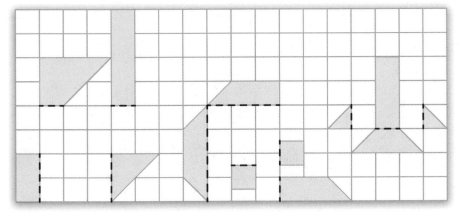

 Select Techniques to Solve Problems (1)(C) What other techniques could you use to solve the problem? Select one and explain how you would use it.

Problem 1 | **Got It?** | **Reflecting a Point Across a Line**

Point P has coordinates $(3, 4)$. If $R_{x=1}(P) = P'$, what are the coordinates of P'?

Learning Animation

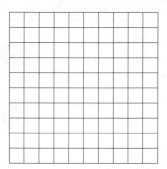

 ELPS Discuss with a classmate the steps you would take to solve the Got It. Use vocabulary from this lesson such as *line of reflection, perpendicular bisector, equidistant,* and *reflection image*.

TEKS Process Standard (1)(D)

 Problem 2 | **Got It?** | **Graphing a Reflection Image**

Graph points $A(-3, 4)$, $B(0, 1)$, and $C(4, 2)$. Graph and label $R_{x\text{-axis}}(\triangle ABC)$.

Learning Animation

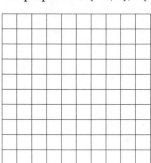

TEKS Process Standard (1)(E)

 Problem 3 | **Got It?** | **Writing a Reflection Rule**

How can you use a reflection rule to describe Triangle 1? Explain.

Learning Animation

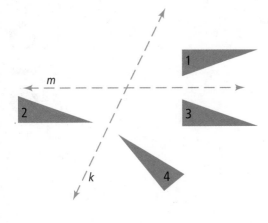

 Problem 4 | **Got It?** | **Using Properties of Reflections**

Can you use a reflection across line t to prove that $\triangle GHJ$ is equilateral? Explain.

Learning Animation

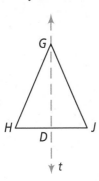

Lesson Check

Do you know HOW?

Use the graph of △FGH for Exercises 1–3.

1. What are the coordinates of $R_{y\text{-axis}}(FGH)$?

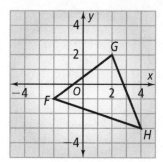

Math
Tools

Online
Practice

Virtual Nerd
Tutorials

2. Graph and label $R_{y=4}(\triangle FGH)$.

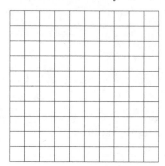

3. A reflection maps $\triangle FGH$ to $\triangle F'G'H'$ with vertices $F'(0, -1)$, $G'(-4, 2)$, and $H'(-6, -3)$. Write the rule that describes this reflection.

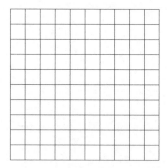

In the diagram, the point (3, 2) is rotated counterclockwise about the origin. The point (x_1, y_1) is the result of a 90° rotation. The point (x_2, y_2) is the result of a 180° rotation, and the point (x_3, y_3) is the result of a 270° rotation. What are the coordinates of (x_1, y_1), (x_2, y_2), and (x_3, y_3)? What do you notice about how the coordinates of the points relate to the coordinates (3, 2) after each rotation?

Interactive
Exploration

Vocabulary
Online

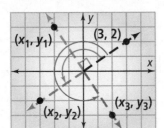

Analyze Mathematical Relationships (1)(F) What mathematical relationships did you identify in the problem? How did you use them to solve the problem?

Problem 1 **Got It?** **Drawing a Rotation Image**

What is the image of $\triangle LOB$ for a 50° rotation about B?

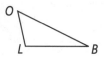

 Learning Animation

 Problem 2 **Got It?** **Drawing Rotations in a Coordinate Plane**

Graph $r_{(270°,\ O)}(FGHI)$.

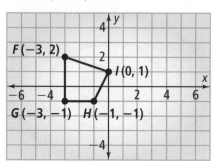

Learning Animation

ELPS Discuss with a classmate your real-world understanding of the word *rotate*. Then write the steps you would use to solve the problem. Trade papers and read your partner's procedure. Combine the best ideas and follow those steps to graph the figure.

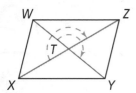 **Problem 3** **Got It?** **Using Properties of Rotations**

Can you use the properties of rotations to prove that *WXYZ* is a rhombus? Explain your answer.

Learning Animation

 **Problem 4** **Got It?** **Identifying a Sequence of Transformations**

In Problem 4, you moved the couch using a rotation and two translations. Identify an alternate sequence of translations and rotations that will move the sofa to a new location in the southwest corner, facing north.

Learning Animation

Lesson 8-3 | Rotations

283

Lesson Check

Do you know HOW?

1. Draw the image of $r_{(70°, P)}(\triangle ABC)$. Use prime notation to label the vertices of the image.

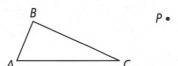

P •

2. In the figure below, A is the center of square $SQRE$. If the sequence of rotations $r_{(x°, A)}(SQRE)$ followed by $r_{(y°, A)}(SQRE)$ maps $\overline{RQ}$ to $\overline{SE}$, what is $x + y$?

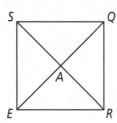

3. $\triangle CDE$ has coordinates $C(0, 2)$, $D(4, 0)$, and $E(0, -2)$. $\triangle FGH$ is the image of $r_{(180°, O)}(\triangle CDE)$. Use a coordinate rule to find the coordinates of $\triangle FGH$ and draw quadrilateral $DFGH$. What is the most precise classification of $DFGH$? Explain.

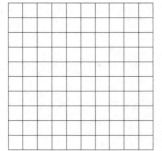

PearsonTEXAS.com

SOLVE IT!

How can you arrange these four identical shapes to make a design that meets Condition 1 but not Condition 2? Sketch your design.

Condition 1: The design is its own rotation image.

Condition 2: The design is its own reflection image.

Interactive Exploration

Vocabulary Online

Connect Mathematical Ideas (1)(F) What prior knowledge did you draw on to solve the problem?

Problem 1 | **Got It?** | **Identifying Lines of Symmetry**

Learning Animation

a. Draw a rectangle that is not a square. How many lines of symmetry does your rectangle have?

b. Is a median of a triangle a line of symmetry for the triangle? Explain.

Problem 2 | **Got It?** | Identifying Rotational Symmetry

a. Does the figure appear to have rotational symmetry? If so, what is the angle of rotation?

Learning Animation

b. Does the figure have point symmetry? Explain.

TEKS Process Standard (1)(E)

Problem 3 | **Got It?** | Distinguishing Between Rotational and Reflectional Symmetry

Identify whether the isosceles trapezoid shown has rotational symmetry, reflectional symmetry, neither, or both. Explain your reasoning.

Learning Animation

 Read the Got It and examine the illustration. Use graph paper or tracing paper to complete the first task of the Got It. Use these materials as a visual aid and explain your reasoning to a classmate.

Lesson Check

Do you know HOW?

1. Study the figure below.

   a. Does the figure appear to have line symmetry? If so, draw its line(s) of symmetry.

   b. Does the figure appear to have rotational symmetry? If so, what is the angle of rotation?

Math
Tools

Online
Practice

Virtual Nerd
Tutorials

2. What types of symmetry does the figure have? Explain your reasoning.

3. Quadrilateral *EFGH* with vertices *E*(1, 4) and *H*(−4, −2) has point symmetry about the origin. Find the coordinates of *F* and *G*. What is the most precise classification of *EFGH*? Explain.

PearsonTEXAS.com

The E on the right is a horizontal translation of the E on the left. How can you use two reflections, one after the other, to move the left E to the position of the right E? Draw in the two lines of reflection. Explain how you found the lines.

Interactive Exploration

Vocabulary Online

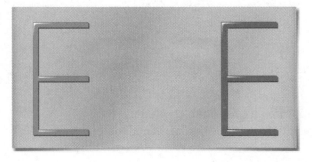

 Create Representations to Communicate Mathematical Ideas (1)(E)
Describe how the representation you made successfully organizes and communicates your solution to the problem.

Problem 1 **Got It?** **Composing Reflections Across Parallel Lines**

a. Draw J between parallel lines ℓ and m. What is the image of $(R_m \circ R_\ell)(J)$? What is the distance of the resulting translation?

Learning
Animation

b. Use the results of part (a) and Problem 1. Make a conjecture about the distance of any translation that is the result of a composition of reflections across two parallel lines.

TEKS Process Standard (1)(G)

 Problem 2 **Got It?** **Composing Reflections Across Intersecting Lines**

a. Use the diagram shown. What is $(R_b \circ R_a)(J)$? What are the center and the angle of rotation for the resulting rotation?

Learning
Animation

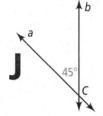

b. Use the results of part (a) and Problem 2. Make a conjecture about the center of rotation and the angle of rotation for any rotation that is the result of any composition of reflections across two intersecting lines.

ELPS Discuss with a classmate. Read the definitions of *congruent* and *sequence of rigid transformations* in the glossary. Confirm your understanding by drawing an example of each on graph paper. Then read and solve the Got It together.

Problem 3 | **Got It?** | **Finding a Glide Reflection Image**

What is the image of $\triangle TEX$ for the glide reflection $(R_{y=-2} \circ T_{<1, 0>})(\triangle TEX)$?

Learning
Animation

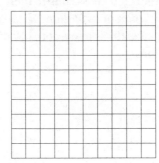

TEKS Process Standard (1)(D)

 Problem 4 | **Got It?** | **Determining Preimages Under Rigid Transformations**

In Problem 4, you determined the vertices of $\triangle ABC$ are $A(-2, 1)$, $B(-1, 4)$, and $C(-4, 2)$ given the transformation $(R_{x\text{-axis}} \circ T_{<5, 0>})(\triangle ABC) = \triangle A''B''C''$.

Suppose that instead the transformation of $\triangle ABC$ is $(T_{<5, 0>} \circ R_{x\text{-axis}})(\triangle ABC) = \triangle A''B''C''$. How would the location of $\triangle ABC$ be affected? Explain your reasoning.

Learning
Animation

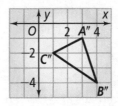

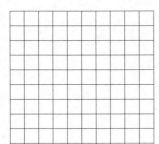

Lesson 8-5 | **Compositions of Rigid Transformations**

295

Lesson Check

Do you know HOW?

1. Sketch an image of Z reflected across line a, then across line b. Is the resulting image a *translation* or a *rotation*? If it is a translation, describe the direction and distance. If it is a rotation, identify the center of rotation and the angle of rotation.

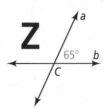

2. $\triangle PQR$ has vertices $P(0, 5)$, $Q(5, 3)$, and $R(3, 1)$. What are the vertices of the image of $\triangle PQR$ for the transformation $(R_{y=-2} \circ T_{<3, -1>})(\triangle PQR)$?

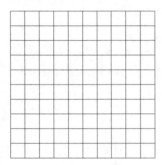

3. The vertices of $\triangle DEF$ are $D(-1, 4)$, $E(2, 6)$, and $F(5, 1)$. The vertices of its image for the glide reflection $(R_{y=a} \circ T_{<-2, 0>})(\triangle DEF)$ are $D'(-3, -6)$, $E'(0, -8)$, and $F'(3, -3)$. What is the value of a?

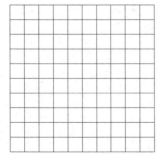

Lesson 8-5 │ Compositions of Rigid Transformations

296

Copyright © by Pearson Education, Inc., or its affiliates. All Rights Reserved.

SOLVE IT!

Suppose that you want to make two identical wings for a model airplane. You draw one wing on a large sheet of tracing paper, fold it along the dashed line, and then trace the first wing. How do you know that the two wings are identical?

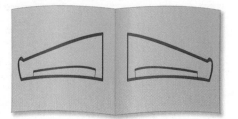

Interactive Exploration

Vocabulary Online

 Apply Mathematics (1)(A) Describe another real-world situation for which you could apply the same mathematical model.

TEKS Process Standard (1)(F)

 Problem 1 | Got It? | **Identifying Corresponding Sides and Angles**

 Learning Animation

Suppose the composition $(R_m \circ T_{<2,\,3>})(\triangle ABC) = \triangle XYZ$. Since $\triangle ABC$ maps to $\triangle XYZ$ by a sequence of rigid transformations, the figures are congruent. List all of the pairs of angles and sides with equal measures.

 Problem 2 | Got It? | **Identifying Congruent Figures**

 Learning Animation

Which pairs of figures in the grid are congruent? For each pair, what is a sequence of rigid transformations that maps one figure to the other?

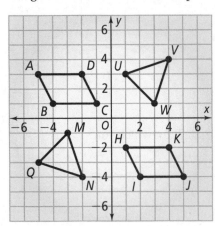

Lesson 8-6 | Congruence Transformations

Problem 3 | **Got It?** | **Identifying Congruence Transformations**

What is a congruence transformation that maps △*NAV* to △*BCY*?

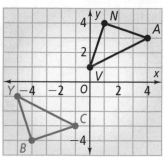

Learning
Animation

ELPS Use familiar language to explain the term *congruence transformation* to a partner. Discuss together the steps that should be taken to solve the Got It. Use tracing paper to trace △*NAV* and use it to work through the sequence of rigid transformations.

TEKS Process Standard (1)(G)

Problem 4 | **Got It?** | **Verifying the SAS Postulate**

In Problem 4, you verified the SAS Postulate. Verify the SSS Postulate.

Given: $\overline{TD} \cong \overline{EN}$, $\overline{YT} \cong \overline{SE}$, $\overline{YD} \cong \overline{SN}$

Prove: △*YDT* ≅ △*SNE*

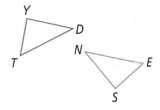

Learning
Animation

Lesson 8-6 | Congruence Transformations

Lesson Check

Do you know HOW?

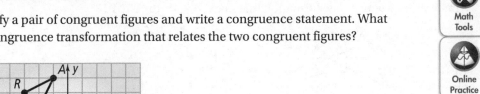

1. Identify a pair of congruent figures and write a congruence statement. What is a congruence transformation that relates the two congruent figures?

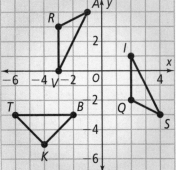

2. Draw $\triangle MCW$ and $\triangle JFP$ so that the congruence transformation $T_{<-2, 1>} \circ R_{x\text{-axis}}$ maps $\triangle MCW$ onto $\triangle JFP$.

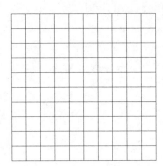

3. A landscape architect uses software to design two flower beds, $\triangle DSQ$ and $\triangle HTV$. Her software does allow rotations. Is there another congruence transformation she can use to check that the flower beds are congruent? If so, provide an example. If not, explain.

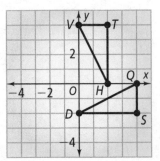

Lesson Check

Do you UNDERSTAND?

Math Tools

Online Practice

Virtual Nerd Tutorials

4. **Vocabulary** How can the definition of congruence in terms of rigid transformations be more useful than a definition of congruence that relies on corresponding angles and sides?

5. **Explain Mathematical Ideas (1)(G)** Is a composition of a rotation followed by a glide reflection a congruence transformation? Explain.

6. **Apply Mathematics (1)(A)** What is an example of a board game in which a game piece is moved by using a congruence transformation? Explain.

TEXAS Test Practice

Multiple Choice

For Exercises 1–4, choose the correct letter.

1. Which of the following best describes a congruence transformation that maps $\triangle FGH$ to $\triangle LMN$?

   A. a reflection only

   B. a translation only

   C. a translation followed by a reflection

   D. a translation followed by a rotation

   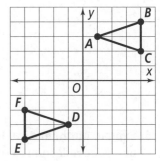

2. Which congruence transformation does not map $\triangle ABC$ to $\triangle DEF$?

   F. $r_{(180°, O)}$

   G. $T_{<0, 6>} \circ R_{y\text{-axis}}$

   H. $R_{x\text{-axis}} \circ R_{y\text{-axis}}$

   J. $R_{y\text{-axis}} \circ R_{x\text{-axis}}$

   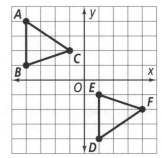

3. A periscope works by reflecting an image twice, each time across a horizontal line. You look through a periscope and see your friend standing 50 ft away. Which of the following is true about the image you see?

   A. Your friend will appear to be upside down.

   B. If your friend waves his right hand at you, it will appear that he is waving his left hand.

   C. Your friend will appear the same size as if you were looking at him from the same distance without the periscope.

   D. Your friend will appear to have rotated 90° counterclockwise.

4. Which congruence transformation maps $\triangle ABC$ to $\triangle DEF$?

   F. $T_{<5, -5>}$

   G. $r_{(180°, O)}$

   H. $R_{x\text{-axis}} \circ T_{<5, 0>}$

   J. $R_{y\text{-axis}} \circ r_{(90°, O)}$

   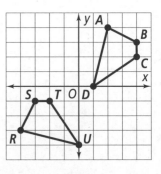

Short Response

5. What is a congruence transformation that maps $ABCD$ to $RSTU$?

The pupil is the opening in the iris that lets light into the eye. Depending on the amount of light available, the size of the pupil changes.

Observe the size and shape of the iris in normal light and in dim light. What characteristics stay the same and what characteristics change? How do these observations compare to transformations of figures you have learned about earlier in the topic?

Interactive Exploration

Vocabulary Online

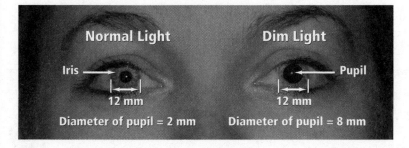

Normal Light   Dim Light

Iris →   ← Pupil

12 mm   12 mm

Diameter of pupil = 2 mm   Diameter of pupil = 8 mm

Connect Mathematical Ideas (1)(F) How does this problem relate to a problem you have seen before?

Problem 1 | **Got It?** | **Finding a Scale Factor**

Learning
Animation

Is $D_{(n,\,O)}(JKLM) = J'K'L'M'$ an enlargement or a reduction? What is the scale factor n of the dilation?

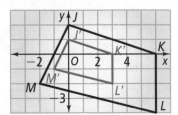

ELPS Read the Got It with a partner. Use your own words to define *enlargement* and *reduction*. Are you familiar with other versions of these words with the same roots? Use support from your partner to solve the Got It.

TEKS Process Standard (1)(G)

 Problem 2 | **Got It?** | **Finding a Dilation Image**

Learning
Animation

a. What are the coordinates of the vertices of $D_{\frac{1}{2}}(\triangle PZG)$?

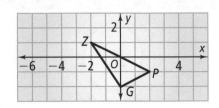

b. How are $\overline{PZ}$ and $\overline{P'Z'}$ related? How are $\overline{PG}$ and $\overline{P'G'}$, and $\overline{GZ}$ and $\overline{G'Z'}$ related? Use these relationships to make a conjecture about the effects of dilations on lines.

 Problem 3 | **Got It?** | **Composing Rigid Transformations, Including a Dilation**

Learning
Animation

In Problem 2, the coordinate rule that describes the dilation is $(x, y) \rightarrow (2x, 2y)$. In Problem 3, the coordinate rule that describes the dilation is $(x, y) \rightarrow (1x, 1y)$. Does each dilation preserve congruence? Explain.

TEKS Process Standard (1)(D)

Problem 4 **Got It?** **Determining the Image of a Dilation Not Centered at the Origin**

Learning Animation

Write a coordinate rule that describes a dilation centered at $P(5, -2)$ with scale factor 3.

Problem 5 **Got It?** **Determining the Image of a Composition of Rigid and Non-Rigid Transformations**

Learning Animation

$\triangle ABC$ has vertices $A(-2, -2)$, $B(0, 1)$, and $C(0, -2)$. Determine the vertices of the image of $\triangle ABC$ after a dilation with scale factor $\frac{1}{2}$ centered at point B, followed by the translation $(x, y) \rightarrow (x, y + 3)$. Graph the image.

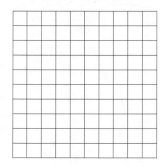

Problem 6 **Got It?** **Using a Scale Factor to Find a Length**

Learning Animation

The height of a document on your computer screen is 20.4 cm. When you change the zoom setting on your screen from 100% to 25%, the new image of your document is a dilation of the previous image with scale factor 0.25. What is the height of the new image?

Lesson 8-7 | Dilations

307

Lesson Check

Do you know HOW?

1. Find the image of each point. Is the dilation an enlargement or a reduction? Explain.

   a. $D_2(1, -5)$

   b. $D_{\frac{1}{2}}(0, 6)$

   c. $D_{10}(0, 0)$

2. What is the equation of the line $D_2(\ell)$?

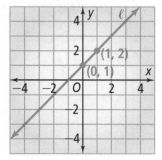

3. An illustrator draws $\triangle ABC$ below to represent the sail of a boat. He first dilates $\triangle ABC$ by a scale factor of $\frac{3}{2}$ to make $\triangle A'B'C'$, and then dilates the image $\triangle A'B'C'$ by a scale factor of 2 to make $\triangle A''B''C''$. Is it possible for the illustrator to map $\triangle ABC$ to $\triangle A''B''C''$ with a single dilation? If so, what is the dilation?

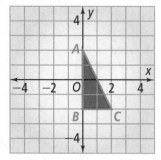

Lesson Check

Do you UNDERSTAND?

4. Vocabulary Describe the scale factor of a reduction.

Math
Tools

Online
Practice

Virtual Nerd
Tutorials

5. Explain Mathematical Ideas (1)(G) The small triangle is the image of the large triangle for a dilation with center *A*. Two students made errors when asked to find the scale factor. Explain and correct each error.

a.

$n = \dfrac{2}{6} = \dfrac{1}{3}$

b.

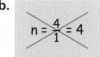

$n = \dfrac{4}{1} = 4$

6. Evaluate Reasonableness (1)(B) A classmate performs a dilation centered at the origin on segment $\overline{JK}$ with endpoints $J(4, 2)$ and $K(-6, 12)$. The classmate determines the endpoints of the image are $J'(6, 3)$ and $K'(-8, 16)$. Is the answer reasonable? Why or why not?

TEXAS Test Practice

Gridded Response

Solve each problem and enter your response on the grid provided.

1. The image of an eraser in a magnifying glass is three times the eraser's actual size and has a width of 14.4 cm. What is the actual width in cm?

For Exercises 2 and 3, the solid-line figure is a dilation of the dashed-line figure. The labeled point is the center of dilation. Find the scale factor for each dilation. Use whole numbers or decimals. Enter your responses on the grid provided.

2.

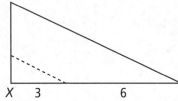

X   3   6

3.

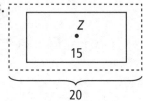

Z

15

20

4. A thumbnail of a photo is 1.7 in. long. The actual photo is 11.05 in. long. What is the scale factor of the dilation?

1.
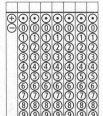

2.
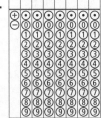

3.
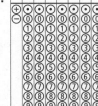

4.
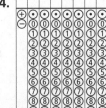

SOLVE IT!

You send a text message with an emoticon to a friend. Your friend replies to your text with the same emoticon. However, the emoticon from your friend looks distorted. Describe the change in the emoticon. How does the change compare to other transformations you have seen?

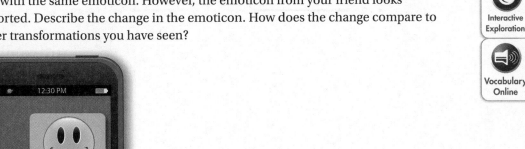

Interactive Exploration

Vocabulary Online

 Use Multiple Representations to Communicate Mathematical Ideas (1)(D)
What is another representation you could you use to present your solution? Explain how the representation communicates the same information.

TEKS Process Standard (1)(E)

 Problem 1 | **Got It?** | **Performing a Stretch**

Learning
Animation

How is the transformation $(x, y) \rightarrow (2x, 3y)$ different from the transformation $(x, y) \rightarrow (3x, 2y)$? Explain.

 Problem 2 | **Got It?** | **Describing a Non-Rigid Transformation**

Learning
Animation

In Problem 2, you wrote the coordinate rule $(x, y) \rightarrow \left(x, \frac{1}{4}y\right)$ to describe the vertical compression $\triangle STW \rightarrow \triangle S'T'W'$.

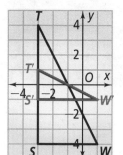

a. Write a coordinate rule that describes a vertical stretch factor of 2.

b. What are the vertices of $\triangle S''T''W''$, the image of $\triangle S'T'W'$ after this transformation? Graph $\triangle S''T''W''$.

c. What single transformation appears to carry $\triangle STW$ to $\triangle S''T''W''$?

Problem 3 **Got It?** Determining the Image of a Composition of Non-Rigid Transformations

Learning Animation

$\triangle ABC$ has vertices $A(-2, -2)$, $B(0, 1)$, and $C(0, -2)$. Determine the vertices of the image of $\triangle ABC$ after the vertical compression $(x, y) \to (x, \frac{1}{3}y)$, followed by a dilation with scale factor 2 centered at the origin. Graph the image.

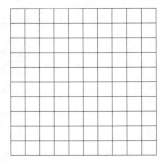

 Read the Got It with a partner. Discuss the given information and what the problem asks for. Together, decide on a procedure to identify the image.

Problem 4 **Got It?** Determining the Preimage of a Composition of Non-Rigid Transformations

Learning Animation

How can you determine the coordinates of the preimage of a figure if you know the image's coordinates after a dilation centered at the origin and then a horizontal stretch?

TEKS Process Standard (1)(A)

Problem 5 **Got It?** Identifying a Sequence of Transformations

Learning Animation

Use the figure in Problem 5. How would the coordinate notation describing the stretch transformation change if the mayor wanted the pool to be wider but not longer, instead of longer but not wider?

Do you know HOW?

1. Find the coordinates of the vertices of $\triangle RST$ after the transformation $(x, y) \rightarrow \left(2x, \frac{1}{3}y\right)$. Graph the image.

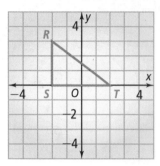

Math Tools

Online Practice

Virtual Nerd Tutorials

2. $\triangle MNP$ has reflectional symmetry and the line of symmetry is $x = 2$. What is the line of symmetry of the image of $\triangle MNP$ after the transformation $(x, y) \rightarrow (3x, 4y)$?

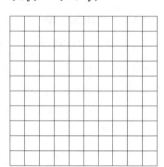

3. In an animated cereal advertisement, a box of cereal starts as Rectangle A and then moves and stretches to become Rectangle B. Describe a sequence of transformations the animator could use to achieve this effect.

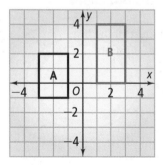

Lesson Check

Do you UNDERSTAND?

4. **Vocabulary** Is it possible for a non-rigid transformation to be both a stretch and a compression? Explain.

Math Tools

Online Practice

Virtual Nerd Tutorials

5. **Analyze Mathematical Relationships (1)(F)** The composition of the stretch $(x, y) \rightarrow (ax, by)$ followed by the compression $(x, y) \rightarrow (cx, dy)$ carries every point in a figure to itself. What relationships must exist among a, b, c, and d?

6. **Select Techniques to Solve Problems (1)(C)** $\triangle JKL$ lies in the first quadrant. You perform a dilation centered at the origin followed by a horizontal stretch. Use number sense to explain why it is not possible for the image of this transformation to lie in the second quadrant.

TEXAS Test Practice

Multiple Choice

For Exercises 1–5, choose the correct letter.

1. A graphic designer is setting up a rectangular region in which to design a poster. He decides to transform the rectangle shown here using a dilation centered at the origin with a scale factor of 2, followed by the horizontal compression and vertical stretch $(x, y) \rightarrow \left(\frac{1}{2}x, 2y\right)$. Which of the following points is a vertex of the image of the transformation?

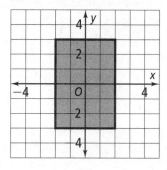

   A. $(-1, 6)$ **C.** $(4, -6)$

   B. $(2, -12)$ **D.** $(-2, -3)$

2. Which transformation may produce an image that is not the same shape as the preimage?

   F. $(x, y) \rightarrow (3x, 3y)$ **H.** $(x, y) \rightarrow (x, 3y)$

   G. $(x, y) \rightarrow (x + 3, y)$ **J.** $(x, y) \rightarrow (x, y - 3)$

3. A student uses software to draw a figure and then transform the figure using the transformation $(x, y) \rightarrow \left(\frac{1}{4}x, y\right)$, followed by a translation up 2 units. Which of the following points of the image has a preimage in the second quadrant?

   A. $(1, 1)$ **B.** $(1, 3)$ **C.** $(-1, 3)$ **D.** $(-1, 1)$

4. Which of the following is true about the transformation $(x, y) \rightarrow (3x, 2y)$?

   F. The image of a square is another square.

   G. The transformation is a dilation.

   H. The image of a figure is a vertical compression of the preimage.

   J. The transformation is a non-rigid transformation.

5. The vertices of $PQRS$ are $P(-1, 2)$, $Q(4, 2)$, $R(4, -1)$, and $S(-1, -1)$. Which transformation of $PQRS$ produces an image that does not intersect $PQRS$?

   A. $(x, y) \rightarrow (1.5x, 3y)$ **C.** $(x, y) \rightarrow (1.5x, y)$

   B. $(x, y) \rightarrow (0.5x, 3y)$ **D.** $(x, y) \rightarrow (0.5x, y)$

Short Response

6. Describe a sequence of a non-rigid transformation followed by a rigid transformation that maps quadrilateral $JKLM$ to quadrilateral $UVWX$.

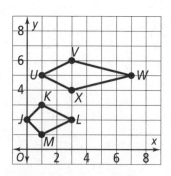

Lesson 8-8 | Other Non-Rigid Transformations

316

SOLVE IT!

A movie theater screen is in the shape of a rectangle 45-ft wide by 25-ft high. Which of the TV screen formats below do you think would show the most complete scene from a movie shown on the theater screen? Explain.

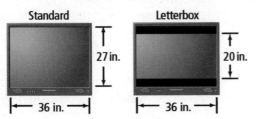

Interactive Exploration

Vocabulary Online

 Apply Mathematics (1)(A) Describe another real-world situation for which you could apply the same mathematical model.

Problem 1 | **Got It?** | Understanding Similarity

Learning
Animation

DEFG ~ HJKL.

  a. What are the pairs of congruent angles?

  b. What is the extended proportion for the ratios of the lengths of corresponding sides?

TEKS Process Standard (1)(F)

 Problem 2 | **Got It?** | Determining Similarity

Learning
Animation

Are the polygons similar? If they are, write a similarity statement and give the scale factor.

a.

b.
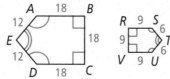

 Problem 3 | **Got It?** | Using Similar Polygons

ABCD ~ EFGD. What is the value of *y*?

Learning
Animation

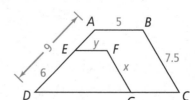

Problem 4 · Got It? · Using Similarity

Learning
Animation

Your class is making a rectangular poster for a rally. The poster's design is 6 in. wide by 10 in. high. What are the dimensions of the largest complete poster that will fit in a space 3-ft wide by 4-ft high?

TEKS Process Standard (1)(A)

Problem 5 · Got It? · Using a Scale Drawing

Learning
Animation

Scale: 1 cm = 200 m

a. The diagram shows a scale drawing of the Golden Gate Bridge in San Francisco. What is the actual height of the towers above the roadway?

b. The Space Needle in Seattle is 605 ft tall. A classmate wants to make a scale drawing of the Space Needle on an $8\frac{1}{2}$ in.-by-11 in. sheet of paper. He decides to use the scale 1 in. = 50 ft. Is this a reasonable scale? Explain.

ELPS Discuss with a classmate. Use estimation to form an opinion for part (b). Then check the facts. If the scale is 1 in. = 50 ft, how many feet are represented by $8\frac{1}{2}$ in.? How many feet are represented by 11 in.? Will a scale drawing of the 605-ft Space Needle fit on the paper?

Lesson Check

Do you know HOW?

Math Tools

Online Practice

Virtual Nerd Tutorials

1. *JDRT* ~ *WHYX*. Complete each statement.

   a. $\angle D \cong$ _?_

   b. $\dfrac{RT}{YX} = \dfrac{?}{WX}$

2. $\triangle FGH \sim \triangle MNP$. Draw and label $\triangle MNP$ such that $\dfrac{PM}{HF} = 0.25$.

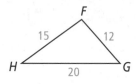

3. The scale drawing at the right is part of a floor plan for a home. The scale is 1 cm = 10 ft. What are the actual dimensions of the dining room and kitchen?

Do you UNDERSTAND?

4. Vocabulary What does the scale on a scale drawing indicate?

Math Tools

Online Practice

Virtual Nerd Tutorials

5. Explain Mathematical Ideas (1)(G) The polygons shown are similar. Two friends write the similarity statements shown. Which friend is not correct? Explain.

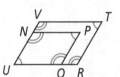

A. $TRUV \sim NPQU$

B. $RUVT \sim QUNP$

6. Justify Mathematical Arguments (1)(G) Is similarity reflexive? Transitive? Symmetric? Justify your reasoning.

Lesson 9-1 | Similar Polygons

321

TEXAS Test Practice

Multiple Choice

For Exercises 1–5, choose the correct letter.

1. You make a scale drawing of a tree using the scale 5 in. = 27 ft. If the tree is 67.5 ft tall, how tall is the scale drawing?

   A. 10 in.   **B.** 11.5 in.   **C.** 12 in.   **D.** 12.5 in.

2. You make a scale drawing of a garden plot using the scale 2 in. = 17 ft. If the length of a row of vegetables on the drawing is 3 in., how long is the actual row?

   F. 17 ft   **G.** 25.5 ft   **H.** 34 ft   **J.** 42.5 ft

3. The scale factor of $\triangle RST$ to $\triangle DEC$ is 3 : 13. What is the scale factor of $\triangle DEC$ to $\triangle RST$?

   A. 3 : 13   **B.** 1 : 39   **C.** 39 : 1   **D.** 13 : 3

4. $\triangle ACB \sim \triangle FED$. What is the value of x?

   F. 4
   G. 4.2
   H. 4.5
   J. 5

   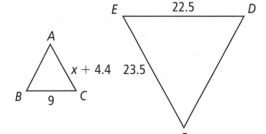

5. $MNOP \sim QRST$ with a scale factor of 5 : 4. If $MP = 85$ mm, what is the value of QT?

   A. 60 mm   **B.** 68 mm   **C.** 84 mm   **D.** 106.25 mm

Short Response

6. Are the triangles at the right similar? Explain.

   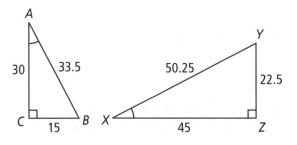

Lesson 9-1 | Similar Polygons

322

SOLVE IT!

Your friend says that she performed a composition of transformations to map △*ABC* to △*A′B′C′*. Describe the composition of transformations.

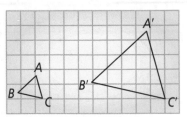

Interactive
Exploration

Vocabulary
Online

 Use Multiple Representations to Communicate Mathematical Ideas (1)(D)
What is another representation you could use to present your solution? Explain
how the representation communicates the same information.

Problem 1 | Got It? | Composing a Rigid Transformation
and a Dilation

Learning
Animation

$\triangle LMN$ has vertices $L(-4, 2)$, $M(-3, -3)$, and $N(-1, 1)$. Suppose the triangle is
translated right 4 units and up 2 units, and then dilated by a scale factor of 0.5 with
center of dilation at the origin. Sketch the resulting image.

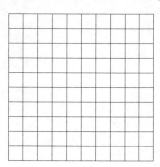

 Problem 2 | Got It? | Describing Transformations

Learning
Animation

What is a composition of rigid and non-rigid transformations that maps
trapezoid *ABCD* to trapezoid *MNHP*?

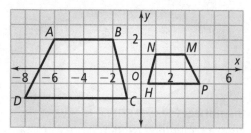

Problem 3 | Got It? | Identifying Similar Figures

If there is a dilation that maps one triangle to another, then they are similar. Determine whether the two triangles are similar. Explain your reasoning.

a. △NSQ with vertices N(0, 3), S(3, 2), and Q(2, 1)
△FRM with vertices F(2, 6), R(6, 4), and M(4, 2)

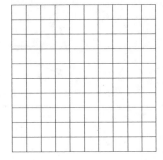

b. △JLT with vertices J(−1, 3), L(−3, 2), and T(−1, 1)
△MIH with vertices M(−2, 6), I(−6, 4), and H(−2, 2)

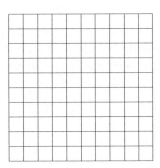

ELPS In this lesson, you've heard how a dilation can map a figure to one that is similar. What do you need to check to make sure the entire figure has been dilated by the same scale factor? Discuss the Got It with a partner. Help each other use the new terms *dilation* and *similar figure* correctly.

TEKS Process Standard (1)(F)

Problem 4 | Got It? | Finding Similarity Transformations

Use the definition of similarity in terms of a similarity transformation to determine whether the triangles are similar. If they are, describe the similarity transformation and write a similarity statement. If not, explain.

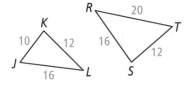

Do you know HOW?

Math Tools

1. What are the coordinates of $(D_{\frac{1}{4}} \circ r_{(180°,\ O)})(\triangle RST)$?

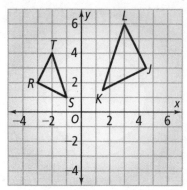

Online Practice

Virtual Nerd Tutorials

2. The length and width of a 5.7 in.-by-3.8 in. rectangular photo are each increased by x in. Can a similarity transformation map one of the images onto the other? Explain why or why not.

3. Identify whether the triangles are similar by determining if there is a similarity transformation that maps one to the other. If the triangles are similar, compare the ratio of their perimeters to the scale factor.

   a. $\triangle PQR$ with vertices $P(3, 0)$, $Q(-4, -2)$, and $R(5, -1)$

   $\triangle STV$ with vertices $S(2.5, 0.5)$, $T(1.5, 0)$, and $V(-2, -1)$

   b. **Figure X**   **Figure Y**

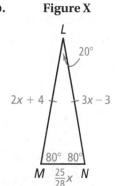
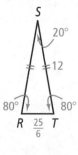

Lesson Check

Do you UNDERSTAND?

4. **Vocabulary** Describe how the word *dilation* is used in areas outside of mathematics. How do these real-world applications relate to the mathematical definition?

Math Tools

Online Practice

Virtual Nerd Tutorials

5. **Analyze Mathematical Relationships (1)(F)** Your classmate claims that the order of the rigid transformation and the dilation that map △RST to △JKL does not matter. Do you agree? Explain.

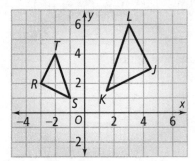

6. **Create Representations to Communicate Mathematical Ideas (1)(E)** For △TUV at the right, give the vertices of a similar triangle after a similarity transformation that uses at least one rigid motion.

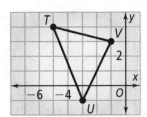

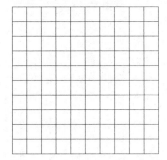

TEXAS Test Practice

Multiple Choice

For Exercises 1–4, choose the correct letter.

1. $MP \neq PK$ and $ML \parallel JK$. Which of the following best describes a similarity transformation that maps $\triangle JKP$ to $\triangle LMP$?

   A. $\triangle JKP$ and $\triangle LMP$ are not similar.

   B. a rotation followed by a dilation

   C. a reflection followed by a dilation

   D. a translation followed by a dilation

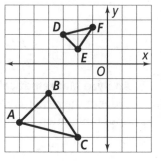

2. Which similarity transformation maps $\triangle ABC$ to $\triangle DEF$?

   F. $R_{x\text{-axis}} \circ D_{0.5}$ **H.** $R_{x\text{-axis}} \circ D_2$

   G. $r_{(270°, O)} \circ D_{0.5}$ **J.** $r_{(90°, O)} \circ D_2$

3. Your video chat software always displays a small video of you in the right-hand corner. You notice that when you hold up a sign for your friend to read, the words and letters that appear on your screen are backward. Is there a similarity transformation that maps the sign you hold up and the image of the sign on your screen?

   A. No; there is no similarity transformation that maps the two figures.

   B. Yes; it is an isometry.

   C. Yes; it is a combination of a dilation and a rotation.

   D. Yes; it is a combination of a dilation and a reflection.

4. Which similarity transformation does not map $\triangle PQR$ to $\triangle STU$?

   F. $r_{(180°, O)} \circ D_2$

   G. $D_2 \circ r_{(180°, O)}$

   H. $D_2 \circ R_{x\text{-axis}} \circ R_{y\text{-axis}}$

   J. $D_2 \circ R_{y\text{-axis}} \circ r_{(90°, O)}$

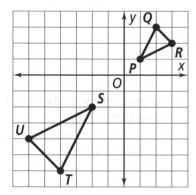

Short Response

5. $\triangle ABC$ has vertices $A(1, 0)$, $B(2, 4)$, and $C(3, 2)$. $\triangle RST$ has vertices $R(0, 3)$, $S(-12, 6)$, and $T(-6, 9)$. What is a similarity transformation that maps $\triangle ABC$ to $\triangle RST$?

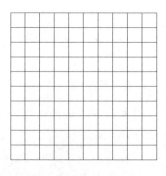

Lesson 9-2 | Similarity Transformations

 SOLVE IT!

Scan page for an interactive
version of this Solve It.

A shop owner needs plywood cut to make a new sign for the front window.
He gives his manager specific instructions to cut a pair of similar triangles.
However, the manager makes a mistake cutting the second triangle and has to
cut a third triangle. Which pair of triangles fits the shop owner's instructions?
How do you know?

**Interactive
Exploration**

**Vocabulary
Online**

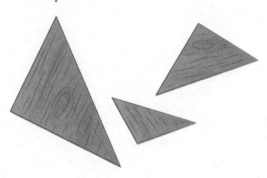

 Select Tools to Solve Problems (1)(C) What other tools could you use to solve the
problem? Select one and explain how you would use it.

Problem 1 | **Got It?** | Using the AA ~ Postulate

Are the two triangles similar? How do you know?

a.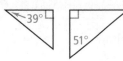

b.

TEKS Process Standard (1)(E)

 Problem 2 | **Got It?** | Verifying Triangle Similarity

Are the triangles similar? If so, write a similarity statement for the triangles and explain how you know the triangles are similar.

a.

b.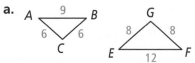

Lesson 9-3 | Proving Triangles Similar

330

TEKS Process Standard (1)(G)

 Problem 3 | Got It? | **Proving Triangles Similar**

a. Given: $\overline{MP} \parallel \overline{AC}$
Prove: $\triangle ABC \sim \triangle PBM$

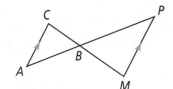

Learning
Animation

b. For the figure above, suppose you are given only that $\frac{CA}{PM} = \frac{CB}{MB}$. Could you prove that the triangles are similar? Explain.

 Problem 4 | Got It? | **Applying Proportionality to Indirect Measurement**

Learning
Animation

In Problem 4, Darius used proportionality to indirectly measure the height of a cliff. Why is it important that the ground be flat to use the method of indirect measurement illustrated? Explain.

ELPS With a classmate, discuss the new expression *indirect measurement* heard in this lesson. What do each of the words *indirect* and *measurement* mean? What do you think they mean when combined in an expression? Why is indirect measurement useful when measuring the height of a cliff?

Do you know HOW?

Math Tools

Online Practice

Virtual Nerd Tutorials

1. Are the triangles similar? If so, write a similarity statement and explain how you know they are similar.

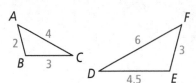

2. **Given:** $\overline{LN} \parallel \overline{ST}$

   Prove: $\triangle LMN \sim \triangle SMT$

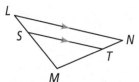

3. Your friend determined that at point S, the measure of the angle from the ground to the top of a tree at point T is the same as the measure of the angle from the ground to the top of a rock formation at point R. Write an expression, in terms of y, for the height of the rock formation, in meters.

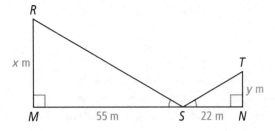

Do you UNDERSTAND?

Math Tools

Online Practice

Virtual Nerd Tutorials

4. Vocabulary How could you use indirect measurement to find the height of the flagpole at your school?

5. Explain Mathematical Ideas (1)(G) Two classmates found the value of *x* for the figure at the right. Which solution is *not* correct? Explain.

A.

$$\frac{4}{8} = \frac{8}{x}$$
$$4x = 72$$
$$x = 18$$

B.

$$\frac{8}{x} = \frac{4}{6}$$
$$48 = 4x$$
$$12 = x$$

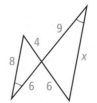

6. Analyze Mathematical Relationships (1)(F) For each theorem and postulate, how are they alike? How are they different? Use precise mathematical language.

a. SAS Similarity Theorem and SAS Congruence Postulate

b. SSS Similarity Theorem and SSS Congruence Postulate

TEXAS Test Practice

Multiple Choice

For Exercises 1–3, choose the correct letter.

1. A farmer needs to find the distance between the beehive B and the cherry tree C, but there is a building in the way. She marks additional points A, X, and Y so that $\overline{XY} \parallel \overline{BC}$ and measures the distances, as shown in the diagram. What is the distance x between the beehive and the cherry tree?

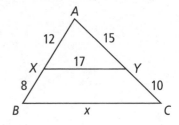

A. $10\frac{1}{5}$ **C.** $11\frac{1}{3}$

B. 19   **D.** $28\frac{1}{3}$

2. Which pair of triangles can be proven similar by the AA ~ Postulate?

F. 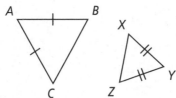   **H.**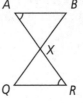

G. 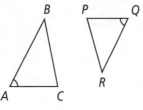   **J.**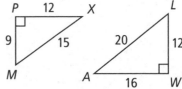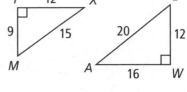

3. $\triangle LMN \sim \triangle PON$. What is the value of x?

A. 36

B. 20

C. 25

D. $28\frac{1}{3}$

Short Response

4. Irene places a mirror on the ground 24 ft from the base of an oak tree. She walks backward until she can see the top of the tree in the middle of the mirror. At that point, Irene's eyes are 5.5 ft above the ground, and her feet are 4 ft from the mirror. How tall is the oak tree? Explain.

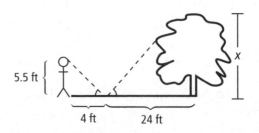

Lesson 9-3 │ Proving Triangles Similar

Draw a diagonal of a rectangular piece of paper to form two right triangles. In one triangle, draw the altitude from the right angle to the hypotenuse. Number the angles as shown. Cut out the three triangles. How can you match the angles of the triangles to show that all three triangles are similar? Explain how you know the matching angles are congruent.

Interactive Exploration

Vocabulary Online

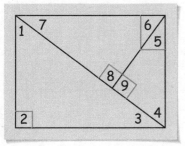

 Connect Mathematical Ideas (1)(F) How does this problem relate to a problem you have seen before?

Problem 1 | **Got It?** | Proving Theorem 9-3

Learning
Animation

In Problem 1, you proved that the altitude of $\triangle ABC$ divides the triangle into two triangles that are similar to the original triangle and to each other. What similarity transformation maps $\triangle ACD$ to $\triangle CDB$? What similarity transformation maps $\triangle CDB$ to $\triangle ABC$?

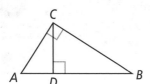

 Problem 2 | **Got It?** | Identifying Similar Triangles

Learning
Animation

a. What similarity statement can you write relating the three triangles in the diagram?

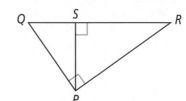

b. From the similarity statement in part (a), write two different proportions using the ratio $\frac{SR}{SP}$.

 The vertices of the big triangle are P, Q, and R. Write the vertices of the two smaller triangles in the same order: right angle, larger acute angle, smaller acute angle. Notice the pattern of the vertices in the ratio $\frac{SR}{SP}$. Write two equivalent ratios. Exchange papers with a friend, read, and compare answers.

 Problem 3 | **Got It?** | Finding the Geometric Mean

Learning
Animation

What is the geometric mean of 4 and 18?

Problem 4 | Got It? | Identifying Proportions in a Right Triangle

In $\triangle TVU$ from Problem 4, shown below, $TX = 2$ and $XV = 8$. Choose a proportion you set up in Problem 4 that will help you calculate UX. Then calculate UX.

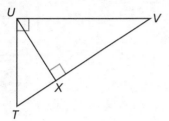

Problem 5 | Got It? | Using the Corollaries

What are the values of x and y?

Problem 6 | Got It? | Finding a Distance

Use the figure in Problem 6. From point D, the robot must turn right and move to point B to put the bottle in the recycling bin. How far does the robot travel from D to B?

Do you know HOW?

Math
Tools

Online
Practice

Virtual Nerd
Tutorials

1. Find the geometric mean of each pair of numbers.

    a. 4 and 9   **b.** 4 and 12

2. In the figure below, $g = 4$ ft and $h = 9$ ft. Find the measures of e, d, f, and j.

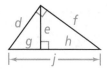

3. The coordinates of $\triangle ABC$ are $A(-2, 4)$, $B(6, 4)$, and $C(6, -2)$. $\overline{BD}$ is the altitude to the hypotenuse of $\triangle ABC$. Find AD and DC. Round to the nearest tenth. (*Hint*: First find AC using the Distance Formula.)

Lesson Check

Do you UNDERSTAND?

4. Vocabulary Identify the following in $\triangle RST$.

a. the hypotenuse

b. the segments of the hypotenuse

c. the altitude

d. the segment of the hypotenuse adjacent to leg $\overline{ST}$

Math
Tools

Online
Practice

Virtual Nerd
Tutorials

5. Justify Mathematical Arguments (1)(G) A classmate wrote an incorrect proportion to find x. Explain and correct the error.

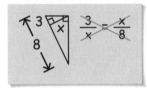

6. Connect Mathematical Ideas (1)(F) How are Corollary 1 and Corollary 2 alike? How are they different?

TEXAS Test Practice

Multiple Choice

For Exercises 1–5, choose the correct letter.

1. The altitude of the hypotenuse of a right triangle divides the hypotenuse into segments of lengths x and 8. The length of the altitude is $x + 2$. What is the value of x?

   A. -2 **B.** 1   **C.** 2   **D.** 8

2. The geometric mean of 7 and some number is $2\sqrt{21}$. What is the number?

   F. 6   **G.** 8   **H.** 12   **J.** $14\sqrt{21}$

3. Which similarity statement is true?

   A. $\triangle WYZ \sim \triangle XZW \sim \triangle XYZ$

   B. $\triangle WYZ \sim \triangle WZX \sim \triangle ZYX$

   C. $\triangle YZW \sim \triangle XZW \sim \triangle XZY$

   D. $\triangle YZW \sim \triangle ZXW \sim \triangle ZYX$

   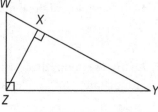

4. What is the value of x?

   F. $2\sqrt{3}$

   G. $4\sqrt{3}$

   H. 4

   J. 6

   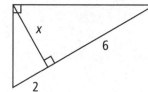

5. Which proportion correctly represents a relationship in $\triangle ABC$?

   A. $\dfrac{AC}{CE} = \dfrac{AB}{BE}$ **C.** $\dfrac{BE}{EA} = \dfrac{EA}{CA}$

   B. $\dfrac{AC}{EA} = \dfrac{AB}{EA}$ **D.** $\dfrac{CB}{CA} = \dfrac{CA}{CE}$

   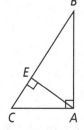

Extended Response

6. What is the perimeter of the large triangle shown at the right? Show your work.

   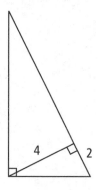

9-5 Proportions in Triangles

 SOLVE IT!

An artist uses perspective to draw parallel lampposts along a city street, as shown in the diagram. What is the value of *x*? Justify your answer.

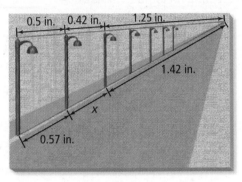

0.5 in.   0.42 in.   1.25 in.

1.42 in.

x

0.57 in.

Interactive Exploration

Vocabulary Online

 Use Representations to Communicate Mathematical Ideas (1)(E)
Describe how the representation you used to solve the problem successfully organizes and communicates your ideas.

Problem 1 | **Got It?** | **Investigating Special Segments of Triangles**

Use your drawing of △ABC from Problem 1. Construct point F on $\overline{AC}$ and a line through F parallel to $\overleftrightarrow{BC}$. Then construct the intersection G of the parallel line with $\overline{AB}$. Write a proportion based on the conjecture you made in Problem 1 and this new segment.

Learning Animation

Conjecture: A line parallel to one side of a triangle intersecting the other two sides divides those sides into proportional segments.

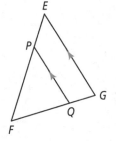 **Problem 2** | **Got It?** | **Proving the Triangle Proportionality Theorem**

Suppose $\overleftrightarrow{PQ}$ is drawn parallel to $\overleftrightarrow{EG}$ of △EFG, intersecting the other two sides. Prove that $\overleftrightarrow{PQ}$ divides those sides proportionally.

Learning Animation

Given: △EFG with $\overleftrightarrow{PQ} \parallel \overleftrightarrow{EG}$

Prove: $\dfrac{EP}{PF} = \dfrac{GQ}{QF}$

Problem 3 | **Got It?** | **Using the Triangle Proportionality Theorem**

Learning Animation

a. What is the value of *a* in the diagram at the right?

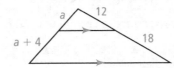

b. In $\triangle XYZ$, $\overline{RS}$ joins $\overline{XY}$ and $\overline{YZ}$ with R on $\overline{XY}$ and S on $\overline{YZ}$, and $\overline{RS} \parallel \overline{XZ}$.
If $\frac{YR}{RX} = \frac{YS}{SZ} = 1$, what must be true about RS? Justify your reasoning.

TEKS Process Standard (1)(F)

Problem 4 | **Got It?** | **Finding a Length**

Learning Animation

In Problem 4, you found that the length
of Site A along the river is 10 yd. What is the
length of Site C along the road?

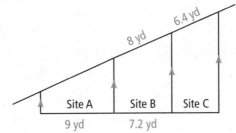

Problem 5 | **Got It?** | **Using the Triangle-Angle-Bisector Theorem**

Learning Animation

What is the value of *y* in the diagram at the right?

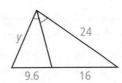

ELPS Discuss with a classmate. The line inside the triangle in the Got It bisects the top
angle. According to the Triangle-Angle-Bisector Theorem, what ratio is the same
as $\frac{9.6}{16}$? How can you find the value of *y*? How can you write another proportion to
check your answer?

Lesson Check

Do you know HOW?

1. Use the figure to complete each proportion.

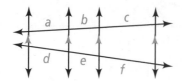

a. $\dfrac{a}{b} = \dfrac{\square}{e}$

b. $\dfrac{b}{\square} = \dfrac{e}{f}$

c. $\dfrac{a}{b+c} = \dfrac{\square}{e+f}$

2. What is the value of x in each figure?

a.

b.

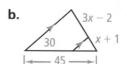

3. A triangular-shaped sunflower garden is enclosed with a fence. One side of the fence is 6 ft longer than another side. The ray bisecting the angle between these two sides splits the third side into 12-ft and 8-ft segments. If the 12-ft segment is adjacent to the longer of the other two sides, what is the perimeter of the fence?

✓ **Lesson Check**

Do you UNDERSTAND?

Math
Tools

Online
Practice

Virtual Nerd
Tutorials

4. **Connect Mathematical Ideas (1)(F)** How is the Corollary to the Triangle Proportionality Theorem related to Theorem 6-7: If three (or more) parallel lines cut off congruent segments on one transversal, then they cut off congruent segments on every transversal?

5. **Justify Mathematical Arguments (1)(G)** A classmate says you can use the Triangle Proportionality Theorem to find both *x* and *y* in the diagram. Do you agree or disagree? Justify your argument.

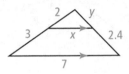

6. **Create Representations to Communicate Mathematical Ideas (1)(D)** How are the Triangle-Angle-Bisector Theorem and Corollary 1 to Theorem 9-3 alike? How are they different?

TEXAS Test Practice

Multiple Choice

For Exercises 1–5, choose the correct letter.

For Exercises 1 and 2, use the diagram at the right.

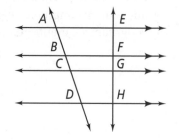

1. The diagram shows a portion of a map of streets in a city. The distance from intersection A to intersection B is 220 yd. It is 260 yd from intersection C to intersection D and 240 yd from intersection G to intersection H. If you are walking from intersection E to intersection F, how far will you have to walk?

A. 203 yd   **C.** 260 yd

B. 238 yd   **D.** 284 yd

2. Which proportion is not true?

F. $\dfrac{BC}{CD} = \dfrac{FG}{GH}$ **G.** $\dfrac{AC}{CD} = \dfrac{EG}{GH}$ **H.** $\dfrac{BD}{FH} = \dfrac{AD}{EH}$ **J.** $\dfrac{AB}{AE} = \dfrac{EF}{BF}$

3. What is the value of y?

A. 2

B. 4

C. 3

D. 6

4. What is the value of x?

F. 3

G. 8

H. 6

J. 12

5. In $\triangle DEF$, the bisector of $\angle F$ divides the opposite sides into segments that are 4 in. and 9 in. long. The side of the triangle adjacent to the 4-in. segment is 6 in. long. To the nearest tenth of an inch, how long is the third side of the triangle?

A. 2.7 in.   **B.** 6 in.   **C.** 13 in.   **D.** 13.5 in.

Short Response

6. In $\triangle QRS$, $\overline{XY} \parallel \overline{SR}$. $\overline{XY}$ divides $\overline{QR}$ and $\overline{QS}$ into segments as follows: $\overline{SX} = 3$, $\overline{XQ} = 2x$, $\overline{RY} = 4.5$, and $\overline{YQ} = 7.5$.

a. Write a proportion to find x.

b. What is the length of $\overline{QS}$?

Scan page for an interactive version of this Solve It.

The right triangles shown have side lengths a, b, and c, where $a < b < c$. Each square has side lengths that correspond to a side length in the right triangles.

Arrange all the pieces of each group to form a square. How do the areas of the two newly formed squares compare? How do you know? What is an equation to relate the areas of the new squares? Explain your reasoning.

Interactive Exploration

Vocabulary Online

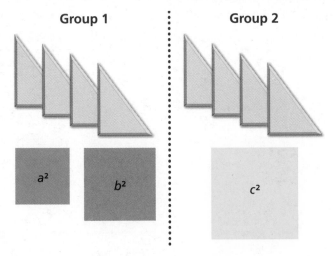

Group 1

Group 2

a^2

b^2

c^2

Create Representations to Communicate Mathematical Ideas (1)(E)
Describe how the representation you made successfully organizes and communicates your solution to the problem.

Problem 1 **Got It?** **Proving the Pythagorean Theorem**

In Problem 1, why can you draw the altitude from point *C* to $\overline{AB}$? Explain.

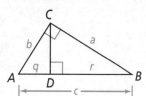

Learning
Animation

 Problem 2 **Got It?** **Finding the Length of the Hypotenuse**

The legs of a right triangle have lengths 10 and 24. What is the length of the hypotenuse?

Learning
Animation

Lesson 10-1 │ The Pythagorean Theorem and Its Converse

348

Problem 3 | **Got It?** | **Finding the Length of a Leg**

Learning
Animation

The hypotenuse of a right triangle has length 12. One leg has length 6. What is the length of the other leg? Express your answer in simplest radical form.

 Problem 4 | **Got It?** | **Finding Distance**

Learning
Animation

The size of a computer monitor is the length of its diagonal. You want to buy a 19-in. monitor that has a height of 11 in. What is the width of the monitor? Round to the nearest tenth of an inch.

Problem 5 | **Got It?** | Identifying a Right Triangle

Learning Animation

a. A triangle has side lengths 16, 48, and 50. Is the triangle a right triangle? Explain your reasoning.

b. Once you know which length represents the hypotenuse, does it matter which length you substitute for *a* and which length you substitute for *b*? Explain.

 Problem 6 | **Got It?** | Using the Distance Formula to Verify Perpendicularity of Segments

Learning Animation

Use △*ABC* shown. How can you verify that $\overline{AC} \perp \overline{BC}$ without using the Slope Formula?

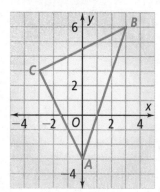

Lesson 10-1 | The Pythagorean Theorem and Its Converse

350

Problem 7 | **Got It?** | **Classifying a Triangle**

Is a triangle with side lengths 7, 8, and 9 *acute*, *obtuse*, or *right*?

Learning
Animation

ELPS Read the Got It and draw a right triangle with legs of 7 and 8. Calculate the length of its hypotenuse. Is 9 *less than*, *greater than*, or *equal to* the length of the hypotenuse?

Lesson Check

Do you know HOW?

1. What is the value of x in simplest radical form?

   a.

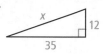

   b.

2. Find an integer j such that the two given integers and j represent the side lengths of an acute triangle. Find an integer k such that the two given integers and k represent the side lengths of an obtuse triangle.

   a. 4 and 5   **b.** 2 and 4   **c.** 6 and 9

3. A contractor is using square and triangular tiles to make the following decoration on a bathroom wall. The square tiles have 1-in. sides, and the triangular tiles are isosceles right triangles. What is the total area of the tiles shown?

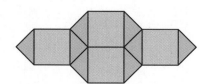

Lesson 10-1 │ The Pythagorean Theorem and Its Converse

352

SOLVE IT!

This map of part of a college campus shows a square "quad" area with walking paths. The distance from the dorm to the dining hall is 150 yd.

Suppose you go from your dorm to the dining hall, to the science lab, to your dorm, to the student center, to the library, and finally back to your dorm. To the nearest tenth of a yard, how far do you walk? Justify your answer. (Assume you always take the most direct routes and stay on the paths.)

Interactive Exploration

Vocabulary Online

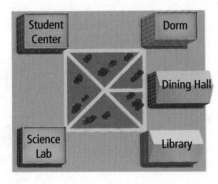

 Connect Mathematical Ideas (1)(F) What prior knowledge did you draw on to solve the problem?

Problem 1 | **Got It?** | **Finding the Length of the Hypotenuse**

What is the length of the hypotenuse of a 45°-45°-90° triangle with leg length $5\sqrt{3}$?

Learning Animation

Problem 2 | **Got It?** | **Finding the Length of a Leg**

a. The length of the hypotenuse of a 45°-45°-90° triangle is 10. What is the length of one leg?

Learning Animation

b. In Problem 2, why can you multiply $\frac{6}{\sqrt{2}}$ by $\frac{\sqrt{2}}{\sqrt{2}}$?

TEKS Process Standard (1)(A)

Problem 3 | **Got It?** | **Finding Distance**

You plan to build a path along one diagonal of a 100 ft-by-100 ft square garden. To the nearest foot, how long will the path be?

Learning Animation

TEKS Process Standard (1)(F)

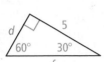 **Problem 4** **Got It?** **Using the Length of One Side**

What is the value of *f* in simplest radical form?

Learning Animation

```
      d    5
   60°   30°
      f
```

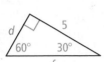 **Problem 5** **Got It?** **Applying the 30°-60°-90° Triangle Theorem**

The artisan in Problem 5 makes another style of pendants in the shape of equilateral triangles. Suppose the sides of this pendant are 18 mm long. What is the height of the pendant to the nearest tenth of a millimeter?

Learning Animation

ELPS Read the problem and underline important words. Draw and label an equilateral triangle to represent the pendant. Discuss with a classmate how to find the height of the pendant. Then, do the calculations needed to find the height.

Lesson Check

Do you know HOW?

Math Tools

Online Practice

Virtual Nerd Tutorials

1. What is the value of x? If your answer is not an integer, express it in simplest radical form.

a.

b.

2. Find the area of the isosceles trapezoid. Express it in simplest radical form.

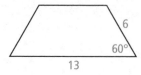

3. A 24-ft ladder leans against a house. The angle the base of the ladder makes with the ground is 45°. For safety reasons, the ladder is moved so that the angle the base of the ladder makes with the ground is 60°. To the nearest tenth of a foot, how much higher does the ladder reach at a 60° angle than at a 45° angle?

SOLVE IT!

What is the ratio of the length of the shorter leg to the length of the hypotenuse for each of △*ADF*, △*AEG*, and △*ABC*? Make a conjecture based on your results.

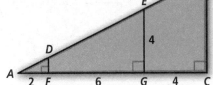

Interactive
Exploration

Vocabulary
Online

Evaluate Reasonableness (1)(B) Explain how you know your solution is reasonable.

TEKS Process Standard (1)(F)

 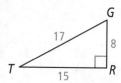 **Problem 1** **Got It?** **Writing Trigonometric Ratios**

What are the sine, cosine, and tangent ratios for ∠G?

G

17

8

T

15

R

 Read the solution to Problem 1 and take notes that will help you solve a similar problem. Then use your notes to help you set up the ratios for each of the trigonometric ratios. Decide the following with a partner: Which side is opposite angle G? What is the length of the hypotenuse? Which side is adjacent to angle G? Then complete the problem.

Problem 2 **Got It?** **Using a Trigonometric Ratio to Find Distance**

For parts (a)–(c), find the value of w to the nearest tenth.

a.
54°
17
w

b.
1.0
w
28°

c.
w
33°
4.5

d. A section of Filbert Street in San Francisco rises at an angle of about 17°. If you walk 150 ft up this section, what is your vertical rise? Round to the nearest foot.

Problem 3 | Got It? | **Using Inverses**

a. Use the figure below. What is $m\angle Y$ to the nearest degree?

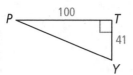

b. Suppose you know the lengths of all three sides of a right triangle. Does it matter which trigonometric ratio you use to find the measure of any of the three angles? Explain.

TEKS Process Standard (1)(A)

Problem 4 | Got It? | **Using the Tangent Ratio**

Use the figure below. What is $m\angle A$ to the nearest degree?

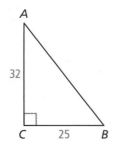

Lesson 10-3 | Trigonometry

363

Do you know HOW?

1. What is the value of *x*? Round to the nearest tenth.

a.

b.

Math
Tools

Online
Practice

Virtual Nerd
Tutorials

2. One angle of a rhombus measures 70°. The diagonal of the rhombus bisecting this angle measures 10 cm. What is the perimeter of the rhombus to the nearest tenth of a centimeter?

3. The height of a local cell tower is 75 ft. A surveyor measures the length of the tower's shadow cast by the sun as 36 ft. What is the measure of the angle the sun's ray makes with the ground? Round to the nearest degree.

You are on the lighting crew for the school musical. You hang a set of lights 25 ft above the stage. For one song, the female lead is on stage alone, and you want all the lights on her. If she stands in the middle of the stage as shown, at what angle from the horizontal should you set lamps A and B? Round to the nearest degree. If you set the lamps for her to stand a few feet closer to the tree, how would each angle change? (Diagram is not to scale.)

Interactive Exploration

Vocabulary Online

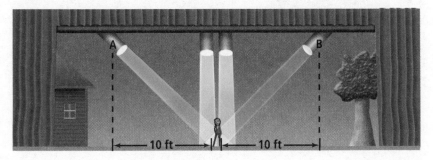

 Select Techniques to Solve Problems (1)(C) What other techniques could you use to solve the problem? Select one and explain how you would use it.

Problem 1 | **Got It?** | **Identifying Angles of Elevation and Depression**

What is a description of each angle as it relates to the situation shown?

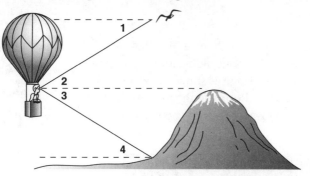

a. ∠2

b. ∠3

ELPS Identify the vertex of ∠2 and the horizontal line from the vertex. Starting at the vertex, in which direction does the nonhorizontal side of the angle go? Is it an angle of *elevation* or an angle of *depression*? Repeat the process for ∠3.

TEKS Process Standard (1)(A)

 Problem 2 | **Got It?** | **Using the Angle of Elevation**

Learning Animation

You sight a rock climber on a cliff at a 32° angle of elevation. Your eye level is 6 ft above the ground and you are 1000 ft from the base of the cliff. What is the approximate height of the rock climber from the ground?

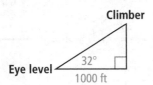

Climber

Eye level

32°

1000 ft

TEKS Process Standard (1)(F)

 Problem 3 | **Got It?** | **Using the Angle of Depression**

Learning Animation

An airplane pilot sights a life raft at a 26° angle of depression. The airplane's altitude is 3 km. What is the airplane's horizontal distance d from the raft?

Lesson Check

Do you know HOW?

For Exercises 1 and 2, use the figure at the right.

1. What is a description of each angle as it relates to the diagram?

   a. $\angle 1$

   b. $\angle 2$

   c. $\angle 3$

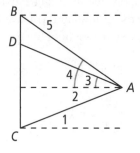

2. If $m\angle 4 = 3(x + 4)$ and $m\angle 5 = 4x - 6$, what is x?

3. A man sitting in a park looks toward the east and sees a kite at an angle of elevation of 40° above the ground. His eye level is 2 feet off the ground. At the same time, a woman sitting 8 feet east of the man at the same eye level looks in the same direction. She sees the kite at an angle of elevation of 45° above the ground. To the nearest foot, what is the altitude of the kite?

 **SOLVE IT!**

Scan page for an interactive
version of this Solve It.

A bike has wheels the same size as the wheel shown below. If the bike wheels are rotating at 320 revolutions per minute, what is the speed of the bike in miles per hour? Explain your reasoning. (*Hint*: 1 mile = 5280 ft)

Interactive
Exploration

Vocabulary
Online

 Evaluate Reasonableness (1)(B) Explain how you know your solution is reasonable.

TEKS Process Standard (1)(D)

 Problem 1 **Got It?** **Naming Arcs**

a. What are the minor arcs of ⊙*A*?

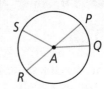

b. What are the semicircles of ⊙*A*?

c. What are the major arcs of ⊙*A* that contain point *Q*?

 Problem 2 **Got It?** **Finding the Measures of Arcs**

What is the measure of each arc in ⊙*C*?

a. $m\widehat{PR}$

b. $m\widehat{RS}$

c. $m\widehat{PRQ}$

d. $m\widehat{PQR}$

Lesson 11-1 | Circles and Arcs

374

TEKS Process Standard (1)(F)

 Problem 3 **Got It?** **Finding a Distance**

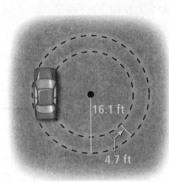
Learning Animation

a. A car has a circular turning radius of 16.1 ft. The distance between the two front tires is 4.7 ft. How much farther does a tire on the outside of the turn travel than a tire on the inside?

16.1 ft

4.7 ft

b. Suppose the radius of ⊙A is equal to the diameter of ⊙B. What is the ratio of the circumference of ⊙A to the circumference of ⊙B? Explain.

 ELPS Read part (a). Work with a partner to rephrase the question in your own words. What is the radius of the outer circle? What is its circumference? What is the radius of the inner circle? What is its circumference? Is the difference between the circumferences the same as the difference between the radii?

 Problem 4 **Got It?** **Finding Arc Length**

Learning Animation

What is the length of a semicircle with radius 1.3 m? Leave your answer in terms of π.

Do you know HOW?

1. What is $m\overset{\frown}{AB}$? What is the length of $\overset{\frown}{BD}$? Leave your answers in terms of π.

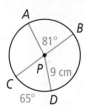

Math Tools

Online Practice

Virtual Nerd Tutorials

2. A piece of plywood was cut out in the shape below for scenery in a school play. The curved side consists of four 90° arcs with the same radius. What is the perimeter of the shape? Round to the nearest tenth of a foot.

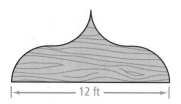

12 ft

3. A 30° arc of $\odot P$ has the same length as a 36° arc of $\odot Q$. What is the ratio of the radius of $\odot P$ to the radius of $\odot Q$?

SOLVE IT!

What is the measure of the angle formed by the slice of pie? Explain your reasoning.

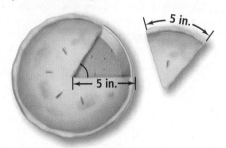

5 in.

5 in.

Interactive Exploration

Vocabulary Online

 Apply Mathematics (1)(A) Describe another real-world situation for which you could apply the same mathematical model.

Problem 1 | **Got It?** | **Finding the Radian Measure of an Angle**

A central angle of a circle has a measure of 1 radian. If the radius measures 6 cm, what is the measure of the intercepted arc?

Learning Animation

Problem 2 | **Got It?** | **Using Dimensional Analysis**

What is the degree measure of each angle expressed in radians? What is the radian measure of each angle expressed in degrees? (Express radian measures in terms of π.)

Learning Animation

a. $\frac{\pi}{2}$ radians

b. $225°$

c. 2 radians

d. $150°$

Problem 3 | Got It? | **Finding the Length of an Arc**

Learning
Animation

a. Use the circle at the right. What is length b to the nearest tenth?

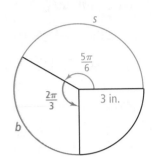

b. If the radius of the circle doubled, how would the arc length change?

ELPS Discuss with a classmate. What is the formula for finding s, the length of an arc? Suppose the radius, r, is doubled to $2r$. How will s change?

Problem 4 | Got It? | **Using Radian Measure to Solve a Problem**

Learning
Animation

Use the diagram in Problem 4. Suppose the satellite orbited 3600 km above Earth's surface and completed an orbit every 4 h. How far would the satellite have traveled in 1 h?

Lesson 11-2 │ Radian Measure

381

Lesson Check

Do you know HOW?

Math
Tools

Online
Practice

Virtual Nerd
Tutorials

1. a. Find the radian measure of an angle of 300°.

b. Find the degree measure of an angle of $\frac{4\pi}{3}$ radians.

2. A car on the outer edge of a Ferris wheel rotates through an angle of $\frac{5\pi}{4}$ radians before stopping. If the radius of the Ferris wheel is 50 feet, how far does the car travel? Round to the nearest foot.

3. A tire on a car has a diameter of 30 inches. Through approximately how many radians will a point on the outside of the tire turn after the car has traveled 1 foot?

PearsonTEXAS.com

In a regular polygon, the radius is the distance from the center to a vertex and the apothem is the perpendicular distance from the center to a side. The area of a regular polygon is half the product of its apothem and perimeter. Each of the regular polygons below has radius 1. Use a calculator to complete the table.

Based on your results, what are the circumference and area of a circle with radius 1? Explain.

Interactive Exploration

Vocabulary Online

Polygon	Number of Sides, n	Length of Sides, s	Apothem, a	Perimeter $(P = ns)$	Area $(A = \frac{1}{2}ap)$
Decagon	10	$2(\sin 18°)$	$\cos 18°$	6.18033 ...	2.93892 ...
20-gon	20	$2(\sin 9°)$	$\cos 9°$		
50-gon	50	$2(\sin 3.6°)$	$\cos 3.6°$		
100-gon	100	$2(\sin 1.8°)$	$\cos 1.8°$		
1000-gon	1000	$2(\sin 0.18°)$	$\cos 0.18°$		

Analyze Mathematical Relationships (1)(F) What mathematical relationships did you identify in the problem? How did you use them to solve the problem?

Problem 1 | **Got It?** | Finding the Area of a Circle

a. What is the area of a circular wrestling region with a 42-ft diameter?

Learning
Animation

b. If the radius of a circle is halved, how does its area change? Explain.

 Problem 2 | **Got It?** | Finding the Area of a Sector of a Circle

A circle has a radius of 4 in. What is the area of a sector bounded by a 45° minor arc? Leave your answer in terms of π.

Learning
Animation

Lesson 11-3 | Areas of Circles and Sectors

386

Problem 3 | **Got It?** | **Finding the Area of a Segment of a Circle**

What is the area of the shaded segment shown below? Round your answer to the nearest tenth.

 Learning Animation

ELPS Read the Got It with a classmate. What is the area of the circle? What is the area of sector *PQR*? What is the area of △*PQR*? With this information, how can you find the area of the shaded segment?

 Problem 4 | **Got It?** | **Finding the Area of a Composite Figure**

The diameter of the circle is 6 m. What is the area of the shaded region?

 Learning Animation

Lesson Check

Do you know HOW?

1. What is the area of the shaded region of the circle? Leave your answer in terms of π.

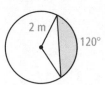
2 m 120°

2. If the area of the shaded region is 16.875π square inches, what is the measure, in radians, of the minor arc that forms the sector?

9 in.

3. A computer animator creates the composite figure below using a circle and a rectangle, with $\overline{AD}$ as both the circle's diameter and a rectangle side. Two sectors of the circle are formed by 36° arcs as shown. If $AB = 4.2$ cm and $AD = 2.5$ cm, what is the area of the figure? Round to the nearest tenth.

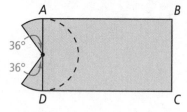
A   B
36°
36°
D   C

SOLVE IT!

The owners of an outdoor adventure course want a way to communicate to all points on the course. They are considering purchasing walkie-talkies with a range of $\frac{1}{2}$ mi. A model of the course is below. Each grid unit represents $\frac{1}{8}$ mi. The base station is at (2, 4). Do you think the owners should buy the walkie-talkies? Why?

Interactive Exploration

Vocabulary Online

 Use Multiple Representations to Communicate Mathematical Ideas (1)(D)
What is another representation you could you use to solve the problem?
Explain why the representation would be useful.

Problem 1 | **Got It?** | Deriving the Equation of a Circle Centered at the Origin

Learning Animation

Describe the graph of $x^2 + y^2 = 25$.

TEKS Process Standard (1)(G)

Problem 2 | **Got It?** | Deriving the Equation of a Circle Centered at (h, k)

Learning Animation

The equation of a circle is $x^2 + y^2 = 49$. What is the standard form of an equation of the circle after its center is translated left 3 units and up 2 units?

Problem 3 | **Got It?** | Writing the Equation of a Circle

Learning Animation

What is the standard equation of each circle?

  a. center $(3, 5)$; $r = 6$ **b.** center $(-2, -1)$; $r = \sqrt{2}$

ELPS Explain how to write the equations for parts (a) and (b) with a classmate. Give reasons for each step. Correct language errors as you speak, using language such as: Let me rephrase ___. A better way to say this is ___.

Problem 4 | **Got It?** | **Using the Center and a Point on a Circle**

What is the standard equation of the circle with center $(4, 3)$ that passes through the point $(-1, 1)$?

Learning Animation

TEKS Process Standard (1)(D)

Problem 5 | **Got It?** | **Graphing a Circle Given Its Equation**

Learning Animation

a. In Problem 5, you found that the center of the circle is $(7, -2)$ and the radius is 8. What does the center of the circle represent? What does the radius represent?

b. What is the center and radius of the circle with equation $(x - 2)^2 + (y - 3)^2 = 100$? Graph the circle.

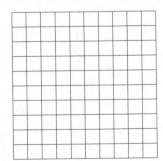

Lesson 11-4 | Circles in the Coordinate Plane

393

Lesson Check

Do you know HOW?

Math Tools

Online Practice

Virtual Nerd Tutorials

1. What are the center and radius of each circle?

   a. $(x - 8) + y^2 = 9$

   b. $(x + 2)^2 + (y - 4)^2 = 7$

2. What is the standard equation of a circle with area 5π and center $(1, -1)$?

3. What is the standard equation of the circle whose diameter has endpoints $A(-1, 1)$ and $B(-1, -5)$?

SOLVE IT!

Draw a diagram like the one below. Each ray from Point *A* touches the circle in only one place no matter how far it extends. Measure $\overline{AB}$ and $\overline{AC}$. Repeat the procedure with a point farther away from the circle. Consider any two rays with a common endpoint outside the circle. Make a conjecture about the lengths of the two segments formed when the rays touch the circle.

Interactive Exploration

Vocabulary Online

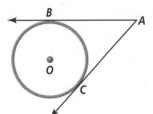

Select Tools to Solve Problems (1)(C) What other tools could you use to solve the problem? Select one and explain how you would use it.

TEKS Process Standard (1)(F)

Problem 1 | Got It? | Finding Angle Measures

a. $\overline{ED}$ is tangent to $\odot O$. What is the value of x?

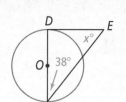

b. Consider a quadrilateral like the one in Problem 1. Write a formula to find x, the measure of the angle formed by two tangents, in terms of c, the measure of the central angle whose radii intersect the tangents.

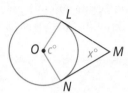

Problem 2 | Got It? | Finding Distance

What is the approximate distance to the horizon that a person can see on a clear day from an airplane 2 mi above Earth? Earth's radius is about 4000 mi.

Problem 3 | Got It? | Finding a Radius

What is the radius of $\odot O$?

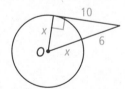

TEKS Process Standard (1)(G)

 Problem 4 **Got It?** Identifying a Tangent

Learning
Animation

Redraw the diagram from Problem 4. If $NL = 4$, $ML = 7$, and $NM = 8$, is $\overline{ML}$ tangent to $\odot N$ at L? Explain.

 Problem 5 **Got It?** Circles Inscribed in Polygons

Learning
Animation

$\odot O$ is inscribed in $\triangle PQR$, which has a perimeter of 88 cm. What is the length of $\overline{QY}$?

15 cm
17 cm

ELPS Read the Got It with a classmate. Discuss together how you know X, Y, and Z are tangent points. What characteristic about tangents to a circle can you use to find PZ and YR? Then, what can you do to find the remaining unknown length of the perimeter? How can you find QY?

Lesson 12-1 │ Tangent Lines

399

Lesson Check

Do you know HOW?

1. If $AC = 12$ and $BC = 9$, what is the radius?

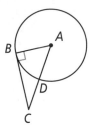

2. The radius of $\odot P$ is 5 units. Tangents are drawn from point R to $\odot P$ at points Q and S. If $\angle P$ and $\angle R$ are right angles, what is PR?

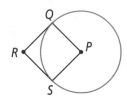

3. $\overline{ED}$ and $\overline{EH}$ are tangents to $\odot F$. $\overline{GH}$ and $\overline{JK}$ are diameters of $\odot F$. If $m\angle DEF = 19$, what is $m\angle FGK$?

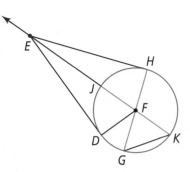

Lesson Check

Do you UNDERSTAND?

4. **Vocabulary** How are the phrases *tangent ratio* and *tangent of a circle* used differently?

Math Tools

Online Practice

Virtual Nerd Tutorials

5. **Evaluate Reasonableness (1)(B)** A classmate insists that $\overline{DF}$ is tangent to $\odot E$. Explain how you can show that your classmate's claim is unreasonable.

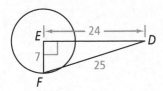

6. **Create Representations to Communicate Mathematical Ideas (1)(E)**
   Draw a circle. Label the center T. Locate a point on the circle and label it R. Construct a tangent to $\odot T$ at R.

TEXAS Test Practice

Multiple Choice

For Exercises 1–5, choose the correct letter.

1. One green on a golf course is a circle with center X. The golf ball is 4 yd outside the edge of the green at point Z. The ball is also 8 yd from the edge of the green at point Y. $\overline{YZ}$ is tangent to $\odot X$. How far from the center of the green is the golf ball?

   A. 4 yd   **C.** 12 yd

   B. 10 yd   **D.** 12.8 yd

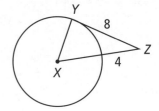

2. Earth's radius is about 4000 mi. To the nearest mile, what is the distance a person can see on a clear day from an airplane 5 mi above Earth?

   F. 63 mi   **G.** 200 mi   **H.** 4000 mi   **J.** 5660 mi

3. $\overline{AB}$ and $\overline{BC}$ are tangents to $\odot P$. What is the value of x?

   A. 73

   B. 107

   C. 117

   D. 146

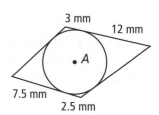

4. The radius of $\odot G$ is 4 cm. Which line segment is a tangent of $\odot G$?

   F. $\overline{AB}$

   G. $\overline{CD}$

   H. $\overline{BF}$

   J. $\overline{FE}$

5. $\odot A$ is inscribed in a quadrilateral. What is the perimeter of the quadrilateral?

   A. 25 mm

   B. 50 mm

   C. 60 mm

   D. 150 mm

Short Response

6. **Given:** $\overline{GI}$ is a tangent to $\odot J$.

   Prove: $\triangle FGH \cong \triangle FIH$

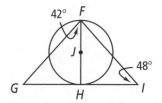

SOLVE IT!

⊙A ≅ ⊙D, and ∠A ≅ ∠D. If BC = 15, what is the length of $\overline{EF}$? How do you know?

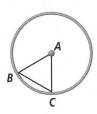

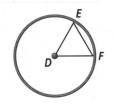

Interactive Exploration

Vocabulary Online

 Connect Mathematical Ideas (1)(F) What prior knowledge did you draw on to solve the problem?

Problem 1 **Got It?** **Using Congruent Chords**

Suppose you are given ⊙*O* ≅ ⊙*P* and ∠*OBC* ≅ ∠*PDF* for the diagram below. How can you show ∠*O* ≅ ∠*P*? From this, what else can you conclude?

Learning Animation

 Problem 2 **Got It?** **Finding the Length of a Chord**

What is the value of *x*? Justify your answer.

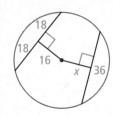

Learning Animation

ELPS Discuss the Got It with a classmate. Compare the lengths of the chords in the figure. What theorems can you use to determine the characteristics of these chords? Be sure to use key vocabulary words and expressions such as *equal to*, *equidistant from*, *congruent*, and *midpoint*.

Lesson 12-2 | **Chords and Arcs**

404

TEKS Process Standard (1)(C)

 Problem 3 | **Got It?** | Investigating Special Segments of Circles

Learning
Animation

In Problem 3, you made the conjecture below. What theorem provides a quick proof of this conjecture?

Conjecture: The perpendicular bisector of any chord of a circle goes through the center of the circle.

TEKS Process Standard (1)(A)

 Problem 4 | **Got It?** | Using Diameters and Chords

Learning
Animation

Trace a coin. What is its radius?

 Problem 5 | **Got It?** | Finding Measures in a Circle

Learning
Animation

In part B of Problem 5, how does the auxiliary $\overline{BA}$, shown below, make the problem simpler to solve?

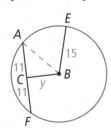

Do you know HOW?

1. In $\odot O$, $m\widehat{CD} = 50$. What is $m\widehat{AB}$? How do you know?

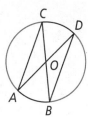

Math
Tools

Online
Practice

Virtual Nerd
Tutorials

2. $\odot W$ and $\odot X$ are congruent. $\overline{YZ}$ is a chord in both circles. If $WX = 6$ cm and $YZ = 4$ cm, what is the radius of $\odot W$? What is the radius of $\odot X$?

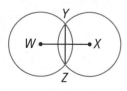

3. Find $m\widehat{AB}$. (*Hint*: You will need to use trigonometry in part (b).)

a.

b.

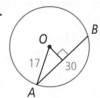

Do you UNDERSTAND?

4. Vocabulary Is a radius a chord? Is a diameter a chord? Explain your answers.

Math
Tools

Online
Practice

Virtual Nerd
Tutorials

5. Analyze Mathematical Relationships (1)(F) ⊙*P* and ⊙*S* are shown in the diagram below. If $\overline{QR} \cong \overline{TU}$, are ∠*QPR* and ∠*TSU* *always, sometimes,* or *never* congruent? Explain.

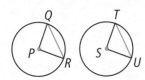

6. Explain Mathematical Ideas (1)(G) What is the error in the diagram?

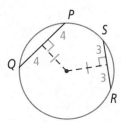

TEXAS Test Practice

Multiple Choice

For Exercises 1–5, choose the correct letter.

1. A bridge across a river is 18 m wide. The bridge is in the shape of a circular arc. In the middle of the bridge, the perpendicular supports are 3 m tall. What is the radius of the arc?

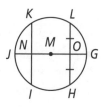

   A. 3 m   **C.** 15 m

   B. 12 m   **D.** 18 m

2. $\overline{JG}$ is the diameter of $\odot M$. Which conclusion cannot be drawn from the diagram?

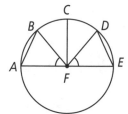

   F. $\overline{KN} \cong \overline{NI}$ **H.** $\overline{JG} \perp \overline{HL}$

   G. $\overparen{LG} \cong \overparen{GH}$ **J.** $\overline{GH} \cong \overline{GL}$

For Exercises 3 and 4, what is the value of x to the nearest tenth?

3.

4.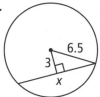

   A. 4.2   **C.** 10.4   **F.** 3.6   **H.** 11.5

   B. 6.6   **D.** 11.6   **G.** 5.8   **J.** 14.3

5. If $\angle AFB \cong \angle DFE$, what must be true?

   A. $\overparen{AB} \cong \overparen{DE}$ **C.** $\overline{CF} \perp \overline{AE}$

   B. $\overparen{BC} \cong \overparen{DE}$ **D.** $\angle BFC \cong \angle DFC$

Short Response

6. **Given:** $\odot A \cong \odot C$, $\overparen{DB} \cong \overparen{EB}$

   Prove: $\triangle ADB \cong \triangle CEB$

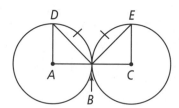

Lesson 12-2 | Chords and Arcs

12-3 Inscribed Angles

Scan page for an interactive version of this Solve It.

SOLVE IT!

Three soccer players practice kicking goals from the points shown in the diagram. All three points are along an arc of a circle. Player A says he is in the best position because the angle of his kicks toward the open goal is wider than the angles of the other players' kicks. Do you agree? Explain.

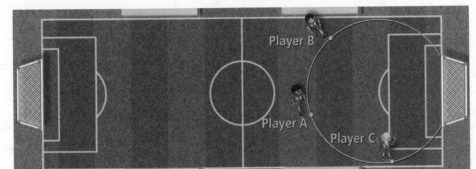

Interactive Exploration

Vocabulary Online

Use Multiple Representations to Communicate Mathematical Ideas (1)(D)
What is another representation you could you use to present your solution? Explain how the representation communicates the same information.

Problem 1 | **Got It?** | **Using the Inscribed Angle Theorem**

a. In ⊙O, what is $m\angle A$?

Learning Animation

b. What are $m\angle A$, $m\angle B$, $m\angle C$, and $m\angle D$?

106° B 100°
A
64° D 90° C

c. What do you notice about the sums of the measures of the opposite angles in the quadrilateral in part (b)?

ELPS Listen as your partner reads parts (a) and (b). Summarize the questions in your own words. Then exchange roles and read part (c). Collaborate with your partner to answer the problems, then discuss your results with the class. Explain the reasons for your conclusion in part (c).

Problem 2 Got It? Using Corollaries to Find Angle Measures

In the diagram, what is the measure of each numbered angle?

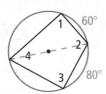

 Learning Animation

 Problem 3 Got It? Using Arc Measure

a. In the diagram below, $\overline{KJ}$ is tangent to $\odot O$. What are the values of x and y?

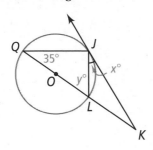

 Learning Animation

b. In part (a), an inscribed angle ($\angle Q$) and an angle formed by a tangent and chord ($\angle KJL$) intercept the same arc. What is always true for these angles? Explain your reasoning.

Do you know HOW?

Math Tools

Online Practice

Virtual Nerd Tutorials

1. Which arc does $\angle A$ intercept? Which angle intercepts $\overset{\frown}{ABC}$?

2. Find each indicated measure for $\odot O$.

   a. $m\angle A$

   b. $m\overset{\frown}{CE}$

   c. $m\angle C$

   d. $m\angle D$

   e. $m\angle ABE$

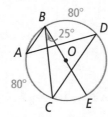

3. What kind of trapezoid can be inscribed in a circle? Justify your response.

Lesson Check

Do you know UNDERSTAND?

4. Vocabulary What is the relationship between an inscribed angle and its intercepted arc?

5. Justify Mathematical Arguments (1)(G) A classmate says that $m\angle A = 90$. Do you agree? Explain.

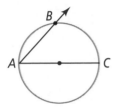

6. Use Representations to Communicate Mathematical Ideas (1)(E) Is the statement below *true* or *false*? If it is true, give a convincing argument. If it is false, give a counterexample.

If two angles inscribed in a circle are congruent, then they intercept the same arc.

TEXAS Test Practice

Multiple Choice

For Exercises 1–6, choose the correct letter.

1. The radius of the circular path shown is 80 meters. Suppose you walk along the arc with measure $z°$. To the nearest meter, how far did you walk?

   A. 108 m   **C.** 176 m

   B. 133 m   **D.** 215 m

2. What is the value of y if the segment outside the circle is tangent to the circle?

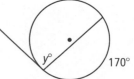

   F. 85   **H.** 190

   G. 95   **J.** none of these

3. What is the value of x?

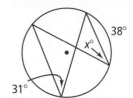

   A. 19   **C.** 38

   B. 31   **D.** 62

For Exercises 4 and 5, use the diagram at the right.

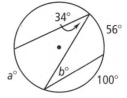

4. What is the value of a?

   F. 34   **H.** 68

   G. 56   **J.** 146

5. What is the value of b?

   A. 28   **C.** 56

   B. 34   **D.** 112

6. The value of r is the solution of the equation $4(r - 100) = 40$. What is the value of s?

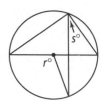

   F. 35   **H.** 70

   G. 55   **J.** 90

Short Response

7. A student inscribes quadrilateral $QRST$ in $\odot D$ so that $m\overset{\frown}{QR} = 86$ and $m\angle R = 93$. What is the measure of $\overset{\frown}{RS}$? Draw a diagram and explain the steps you took to find the answer.

SOLVE IT!

Find $m\angle 1$ and the sum of the measures of $\overset{\frown}{AD}$ and $\overset{\frown}{BC}$. What is the relationship between the measures? How do you know?

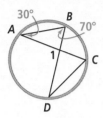

Interactive Exploration

Vocabulary Online

 Connect Mathematical Ideas (1)(F) How does this problem relate to a problem you have seen before?

TEKS Process Standard (1)(C)

 Problem 1 | **Got It?** | Investigating Special Angles of Circles

Construct a circle and a pair of chords that intersect inside it. What do you notice about the mean of the measures of the two intercepted arcs?

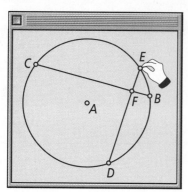

Learning Animation

Problem 2 | **Got It?** | Finding Angle Measures

What is the value of each variable?

Learning Animation

a.

b.

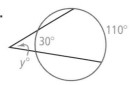

c.

ELPS Describe one of the diagrams in the Got It to a partner. What are the lines in each diagram called? How do they differ? Discuss a method to solve each part of the problem.

Lesson 12-4 | Angle Measures and Segment Lengths

416

Problem 3 — Got It? — Finding an Arc Measure

A departing space probe sends back a picture of Earth as it crosses Earth's equator. The angle formed by the two tangents to the equator is about 20°.

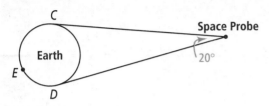

a. What is the measure of the arc of the equator that is visible to the space probe?

b. In Problem 3, a 162.5° arc could be viewed from the geostationary satellite. Is the probe or the satellite closer to Earth? Explain.

TEKS Process Standard (1)(F)

Problem 4 — Got It? — Finding Segment Lengths

What is the value of the variable in ⊙*P* to the nearest tenth?

a.

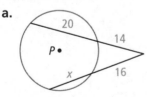

b.

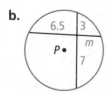

Lesson Check

Do you know HOW?

1. What are the values of x, y, and z, to the nearest tenth?

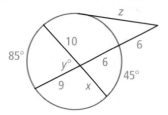

Math
Tools

Online
Practice

Virtual Nerd
Tutorials

2. The measure of the angle formed by two tangents to a circle is 80. What are the measures of the intercepted arcs?

3. Find the diameter of $\odot O$. A line that appears to be tangent is tangent. Round your answer to the nearest tenth.

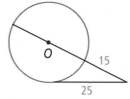

Lesson Check

Do you know UNDERSTAND?

Math
Tools

Online
Practice

Virtual Nerd
Tutorials

4. Vocabulary Describe the difference between a *secant* and a *tangent*.

5. Evaluate Reasonableness (1)(B) The diagram from Exercise 1 is shown at the right. Is it possible to find the measures of the unmarked arcs? Explain.

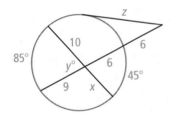

6. Justify Mathematical Arguments (1)(G) To find the value of *x*, a student wrote the equation $(7.5)6 = x^2$. What error did the student make? Write the correct equation.

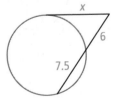

Multiple Choice

For Exercises 1–6, choose the correct letter.

1. A landscaping company is planning a circular garden and a stone path in the shape of an equilateral triangle. The path will have sides of length 6 m and be inscribed in the circular garden. What is the diameter of the circular garden?

   A. 5.2 m   **B.** 6 m   **C.** 6.9 m   **D.** 7.5 m

2. In the figure at the right, what is $m\angle C$?

   F. 15   **H.** 50

   G. 35   **J.** 65

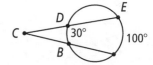

3. In the figure at the right, what is the value of x?

   A. 45   **C.** 75

   B. 60   **D.** 90

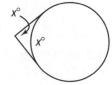

4. In the figure at the right, what is the value of z in terms of y?

   F. $0.4y$ **H.** $y - 1$

   G. $0.8y$ **J.** $1.25y$

5. Which of the following statements is false?

   A. Every chord is part of a secant.   **C.** Every chord is a diameter.

   B. Every diameter is part of a secant.   **D.** Every diameter is a chord.

6. In the figure at the right, what is $m\overset{\frown}{ABC}$ in terms of x?

   F. $180 + x$ **H.** $2(180 + x)$

   G. $180 - x$ **J.** $360 - x$

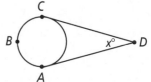

Short Response

7. Use $\odot O$ to prove that $\triangle AED \sim \triangle BEC$.

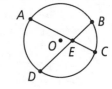

 **SOLVE IT!**

A stage is being set up for a concert at the arena. The stage is made up of blocks with tops that are congruent right triangles. The tops of two of the blocks, when put together, make an 8 ft-by-8 ft square. The band has requested that the stage be arranged to form the shape of an arrow. Draw a diagram that shows how the stage could be laid out in the shape of an arrow with an area of at least 1000 ft^2 but no more than 1400 ft^2.

Interactive Exploration

Vocabulary Online

8 ft   8 ft

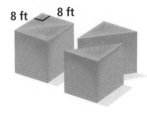

 Use Representations to Communicate Mathematical Ideas (1)(E)
Describe how the representation you used to solve the problem successfully organizes and communicates your ideas.

Problem 1 | **Got It?** | **Finding the Area of a Parallelogram**

What is the area of a parallelogram with base length 12 m and height 9 m?

Learning
Animation

TEKS Process Standard (1)(F)

 Problem 2 | **Got It?** | **Finding a Missing Dimension**

A parallelogram has sides 15 cm and 18 cm. The height corresponding to a 15-cm base is 9 cm. What is the height corresponding to an 18-cm base?

Learning
Animation

Problem 3 | **Got It?** | Finding the Area of a Triangle

Learning Animation

What is the area of the triangle?

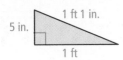

1 ft 1 in.

5 in.

1 ft

 ELPS Find a partner and listen as your partner summarizes the three steps used in Problem 3 to find the area. List the new vocabulary words used such as *base* and *height of a triangle*. Then describe these terms as your partner listens. What dimensions of a triangle do you need to know in order to calculate its area? How can you express both dimensions in the same units?

TEKS Process Standard (1)(C)

 Problem 4 | **Got It?** | Finding the Area of a Composite Figure

Learning Animation

What is the area of the figure?

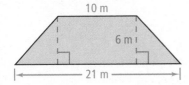

10 m

6 m

21 m

Lesson Check

Do you know HOW?

1. Find the area of each figure.

a.
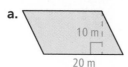

b.

Math
Tools

Online
Practice

Virtual Nerd
Tutorials

2. Graph the lines: $y = -x$; $y = -6$; $y = -x - 4$; $y = 6$.

a. Identify the figure enclosed by the lines.

b. Find the area of the figure enclosed by the lines.

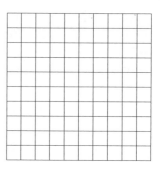

3. The Spirit Club is decorating a rectangular-shaped banner for a pep rally. The non-shaded region of the banner is going to be covered in glitter. Find the area of the banner that will be covered in glitter.

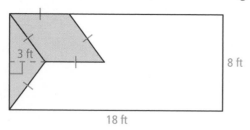

Lesson 13-1 │ **Areas of Parallelograms and Triangles**

424

Scan page for an interactive
version of this Solve It.

**SOLVE IT!**

You can divide the trapezoid and kite into pieces and rearrange the pieces to make new figures. How can you use the new figures to find the areas of the original figures? Explain your reasoning.

 Interactive Exploration

 Vocabulary Online

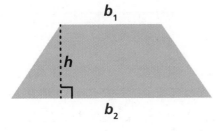

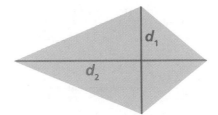

 Connect Mathematical Ideas (1)(F) How does this problem relate to a problem you have seen before?

TEKS Process Standard (1)(A)

Problem 1 | Got It? | Area of a Trapezoid

What is the area of a trapezoid with height 7 cm and bases 12 cm and 15 cm?

Learning
Animation

Problem 2 | Got It? | Finding Area Using a Right Triangle

In the figure below, suppose h decreases so that $m\angle P = 45$ while angles R and Q and the bases stay the same. What is the area of trapezoid $PQRS$?

Learning
Animation

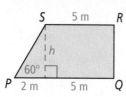

Problem 3 | Got It? | Finding the Area of a Kite

What is the area of a kite with diagonals that are 12 in. and 9 in. long?

Learning
Animation

 Sketch a kite with diagonals of 12 in. and 9 in. Then circumscribe a rectangle around your kite. How does the area of the kite compare to the area of the rectangle? Compare your diagram with a classmate's diagram. How do the kites differ? How do the rectangles differ? Then read the Got It. Refer to your diagram to solve the problem. How does the diagram help you understand the formula for the area of a kite?

Problem 4 | **Got It?** | Finding the Area of a Rhombus

Learning Animation

A rhombus has sides 10 cm long. If the longer diagonal is 16 cm, what is the area of the rhombus?

TEKS Process Standard (1)(B)

 Problem 5 | **Got It?** | Finding the Area of a Composite Figure

Learning Animation

In Problem 5, you found the area of the figure by summing the areas of the trapezoids and the kite. Describe an alternative plan for finding the area of the figure.

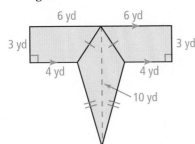

Lesson Check

Do you know HOW?

1. Find the area of each figure.

a.
15 in.
18 in.
27 in.

b.
3 ft
5 ft

c.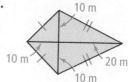
10 m
10 m
20 m
10 m

Math
Tools

Online
Practice

Virtual Nerd
Tutorials

2. The height of a trapezoid is 8 ft and its area is 116 ft². One base of the trapezoid is 1 ft shorter than twice the length of the other base. Find the length of each base.

3. The owner of a tuxedo company used two congruent isosceles trapezoids and a square to create business cards in the shape of a bow-tie. Find the area of the business card to the nearest square centimeter.

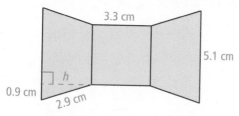
3.3 cm
5.1 cm
h
0.9 cm
2.9 cm

SOLVE IT!

You want to build a koi pond. For the border, you plan to use 3-ft-long pieces of wood. You have 12 pieces that you can connect together at any angle, including a straight angle. If you want to maximize the area of the pond, in what shape should you arrange the pieces? Explain your reasoning.

Interactive Exploration

Vocabulary Online

 Use a Problem-Solving Model (1)(B) Evaluate your problem-solving model. Which parts were helpful? Which would you want to revise? Explain.

Problem 1 | Got It? | Finding Angle Measures

At the right, a portion of a regular octagon has radii and an apothem drawn. What is the measure of each numbered angle?

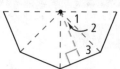

Learning Animation

ELPS Read the Got It with a partner. Take turns reading and answering the following questions. What makes an octagon regular? What is the difference between a radius and an apothem? What is the name and measure of $\angle 1$? What methods can be used to find $\angle 3$?

Problem 2 | Got It? | Finding the Area of a Regular Polygon

a. What is the area of a regular pentagon with an 8-cm apothem and 11.6-cm sides?

Learning Animation

b. If the side of a regular polygon is reduced to half its length, how does the perimeter of the polygon change? Explain.

TEKS Process Standard (1)(D)

Problem 3 | **Got It?** | Using Special Triangles to Find Area

The side of a regular hexagon is 16 ft. What is the area of the hexagon? Round your answer to the nearest square foot.

Learning Animation

Problem 4 | **Got It?** | Finding the Area of a Composite Figure

In Problem 4, you found the area of the figure by finding the area of a hexagon and a triangle, and then finding the area of the four figures combined. Describe two alternative compositions of shapes that you could use to find the area of the figure.

Learning Animation

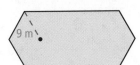

9 m

Lesson 13-3 | Areas of Regular Polygons

Do you know HOW?

1. What is the area of each regular polygon? Round your answer to the nearest tenth.

   a.

   3 ft

   b.
   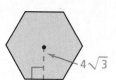
   $4\sqrt{3}$

Math
Tools

Online
Practice

Virtual Nerd
Tutorials

2. The face of a stop sign is a regular octagon. If each side is 14.9 in. long, and the area is 1072.8 in.^{2}, find the length of the apothem.

3. Ceramic tile is being used to cover two 6 ft-by-4 ft rectangular walls. The tiles are in the shape of equilateral triangles with 6-in. sides. A box of tiles contains 20 tiles. How many boxes of tiles will be needed to cover both walls?

SOLVE IT!

On a piece of grid paper, draw a 3 unit-by-4 unit rectangle. Then draw three different rectangles, each similar to the original rectangle. Label them I, II, and III. Use your drawings to complete the table at the right.

Rectangle	Perimeter	Area
Original		
I		
II		
III		

Interactive Exploration

Vocabulary Online

Use the information from the table above to complete the table at the right.

Rectangle	Scale Factor	Ratio of Perimeters	Ratio of Areas
I to Original			
II to Original			
III to Original			

How do the ratios of perimeters and the ratios of areas compare with the scale factors?

 Connect Mathematical Ideas (1)(F) What prior knowledge did you draw on to solve the problem?

Problem 1 | **Got It?** | Analyzing Proportional Dimensional Changes

Learning Animation

The floor plan of a rectangular room has a scale of 1 in. : 2.5 ft. In the floor plan, the room is 4 in. wide by 6 in. long. What is the area of the actual room?

Problem 2 | **Got It?** | Finding Ratios in Similar Figures

Learning Animation

Two similar polygons have corresponding sides in the ratio 5 : 7.

a. What is the ratio (larger to smaller) of their perimeters?

b. What is the ratio (larger to smaller) of their areas?

Lesson 13-4 │ Perimeters and Areas of Similar Figures

Problem 3 | **Got It?** | **Finding Areas Using Similar Figures**

The scale factor of two similar parallelograms is $\frac{3}{4}$. The area of the larger parallelogram is 96 in.^{2}. What is the area of the smaller parallelogram?

Problem 4 | Got It? | Applying Area Ratios

Learning
Animation

a. The scale factor of the dimensions of two similar pieces of window glass is 3 : 5. The smaller piece costs $2.50. How much should the larger piece cost?

b. In Problem 4, you found that the students could expect to harvest about 81 bushels of vegetables because each dimension of the new plot of land was 2.5 times the corresponding dimension of the original plot. Why is it important that *each* dimension is 2.5 times the corresponding dimension of the original plot? Explain.

ELPS Listen as a volunteer reads part (b) of the Got It. Discuss the problem with a partner. Summarize the given information and what you need to find. Draw a rectangle to represent the first plot. Draw another rectangle that is 2.5 times as long as the first. Is it similar? How can you make the second rectangle similar to the first?

Problem 5 Got It? Finding Perimeter Ratios

The areas of two similar rectangles are 1875 ft^2 and 135 ft^2. What is the ratio of their perimeters?

Learning
Animation

 Problem 6 Got It? Analyzing Nonproportional Dimension Changes

A rectangular playground is 21.5 feet in length and has an area of 387 ft^2. How does doubling the width affect the area? What is the new area?

Learning
Animation

Do you know HOW?

1. The figures in each pair are similar. What is the ratio of the perimeters and the ratio of the areas?

a.

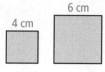

4 cm   6 cm

b.

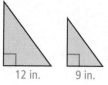

12 in.   9 in.

Math
Tools

Online
Practice

Virtual Nerd
Tutorials

2. The areas of two similar rhombuses are 48 m² and 128 m². What is the ratio of their perimeters?

3. Suppose $\overline{AB}$ is the base of isosceles $\triangle ABC$, $\overline{XY}$ is the base of isosceles $\triangle XYZ$, and $\overline{AB} \cong \overline{XY}$. The height of $\triangle XYZ$ is 4 times the height of $\triangle ABC$.

a. What is the ratio of the area of $\triangle ABC$ to the area of $\triangle XYZ$?

b. Are $\triangle ABC$ and $\triangle XYZ$ similar triangles? How do you know?

SOLVE IT!

The pennant below is in the shape of an isosceles triangle. The measure of the vertex angle is 20. What is the area of the pennant? How do you know?

Interactive Exploration

Vocabulary Online

10 in.

Apply Mathematics (1)(A) Describe another real-world situation for which you could apply the same mathematical model.

Problem 1 | **Got It?** | **Finding Area**

What is the area of a regular pentagon with 4-in. sides? Round your answer to the nearest square inch.

Learning Animation

TEKS Process Standard (1)(C)

 Problem 2 | **Got It?** | **Finding Area**

 Learning Animation

a. A tabletop has the shape of a regular decagon with a radius of 9.5 in. What is the area of the tabletop to the nearest square inch?

b. Suppose the radius of a regular polygon is doubled. How does the area of the polygon change? Explain.

 After solving part (a), read part (b) with a partner. Refer to the road sign in Problem 2. Why is it a regular polygon? Brainstorm other signs you see along the road or in school. What do they mean? Solve part (b) using one of the regular polygons in your list.

 Problem 3 | **Got It?** | **Finding Area**

Learning Animation

What is the area of the triangle? Round your answer to the nearest square inch.

10 in.

34°

16 in.

Do you know HOW?

1. What is the area of each regular polygon? Round your answers to the nearest tenth.

a.

4 m

b.

6 cm

Math Tools

Online Practice

Virtual Nerd Tutorials

2. The area of $\triangle ABC$ is 22.5 in.^{2}. What is the measure of $\angle CAB$, to the nearest degree?

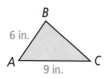

B

6 in.

A

9 in.

C

3. Initial designs for a kitchen remodel specify an island in the shape of a regular hexagon with 2.5-ft sides. The homeowners prefer that the island be a regular pentagon, with 3-ft sides. Which island has the greater area and by how much?

SOLVE IT!

A jewelry designer needs a pattern that she can fold to make cube-shaped boxes for packaging jewelry. The designer wants the boxes to have a ribbon that appears to be joined continuously around the box. Which of the following patterns will work? Explain your reasoning.

Interactive Exploration

Vocabulary Online

A

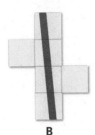

B

C

D

Select Tools to Solve Problems (1)(C) What other tools could you use to solve the problem? Select one and explain how you would use it.

Problem 1 | **Got It?** | **Using Euler's Formula**

For each polyhedron, use Euler's Formula to find the missing number.

a.

faces:

edges: 30

vertices: 20

b.

faces: 20

edges:

vertices: 12

 Problem 2 | **Got It?** | **Verifying Euler's Formula in Two Dimensions**

a. How can you verify Euler's Formula $F + V = E + 2$ for the solid at the right?

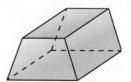

b. Draw a net for the solid.

c. How can you verify Euler's Formula $F + V = E + 1$ for your two-dimensional net?

Problem 3 **Got It?** Describing a Cross Section

For the solid shown, what is the cross section formed by each of the following planes?

a. a horizontal plane

b. a vertical plane that divides the solid in half

ELPS Read the Got It with a classmate. Discuss the meaning of the term *cross section*. Imagine looking at the solid from the top down. What shape do you see? If you slice off part of the solid with a horizontal cut, what shape will you see? Now look at the solid from the side. If you cut away the half that is closest to you with a vertical cut, what shape will you see?

TEKS Process Standard (1)(E)

Problem 4 **Got It?** **Drawing a Cross Section**

Draw the cross section formed by a horizontal plane intersecting the left and right faces of the cube. What shape is the cross section?

Learning Animation

Problem 5 **Got It?** **Identifying Cross Sections of Pyramids, Cones, and Spheres**

Draw and identify the cross section formed when a cone is intersected by a plane perpendicular to the base and passing through the vertex.

Learning Animation

Lesson 14-1 | Three-Dimensional Figures and Cross Sections

TEKS Process Standard (1)(D)

 Problem 6 | **Got It?** | Rotating Two-Dimensional Shapes

Learning Animation

Identify the three-dimensional object generated by rotating a two-dimensional shape as described.

a. Rotate a circle around a line that passes through the center of the circle.

b. Rotate a right triangle around a line that passes through one of the legs of the triangle.

Lesson 14-1 | Three-Dimensional Figures and Cross Sections

457

Do you know HOW?

1. A polyhedron is shown at the right.

   a. How many vertices, edges, and faces does the solid have? Use your results to verify Euler's Formula.

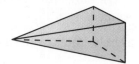

Math Tools

Online Practice

Virtual Nerd Tutorials

   b. Draw a net for the solid. Verify Euler's Formula for the net.

2. What is the cross section formed by the cube and the plane containing the diagonals of a pair of opposite faces?

3. Draw and describe three different cross sections that can be formed by a plane intersecting this solid. Identify any polygons.

Lesson Check

Do you UNDERSTAND?

4. **Vocabulary** Suppose you build a polyhedron from two octagons and eight squares. Without using Euler's Formula, how many edges does the solid have? Explain.

5. **Explain Mathematical Ideas (1)(G)** Your class is drawing polyhedrons. Which figure does not belong in the diagram below? Explain.

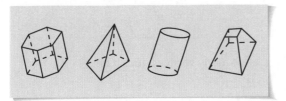

6. **Justify Mathematical Arguments (1)(G)** Can an object formed by rotating a polygon around a line ever be a polyhedron? Justify your answer.

TEXAS Test Practice

Multiple Choice

For Exercises 1–5, choose the correct letter.

1. The marketing department at a sporting equipment company wants to sell ping pong balls in new boxes with 8 faces, 12 vertices, and 18 edges. Which of the following is a net for a box that meets their criteria?

A.

C.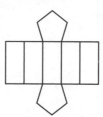

B.

D.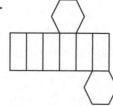

2. A polyhedron has 25 faces and 36 edges. How many vertices does it have?

   F. 11   **G.** 12   **H.** 13   **J.** 14

3. A polyhedron with volume 60 in.^{3} has 6 vertices and 9 edges. How many faces does it have?

   A. 3   **B.** 5   **C.** 7   **D.** 9

4. What is the cross section formed by a plane intersecting a triangular pyramid parallel to its base?

   F. triangle   **G.** square   **H.** rectangle   **J.** pentagon

5. A plane intersects a cube. Which of the following cannot be formed by this intersection?

   A. triangle   **B.** square   **C.** hexagon   **D.** octagon

Short Response

6. An octahedron is a polyhedron with eight congruent triangular faces. How many edges and vertices does an octahedron have?

14-2 Surface Areas of Prisms and Cylinders

SOLVE IT!

A piece of string is wrapped once around an empty paper towel tube. The ends of the string are attached to each end of the tube as shown. How long is the piece of string? Justify your reasoning.

Interactive Exploration

Vocabulary Online

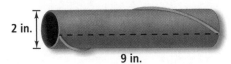

2 in.

9 in.

Use Multiple Representations to Communicate Mathematical Ideas (1)(D)
What is another representation you could use to solve the problem? Explain why the representation would be useful.

TEKS Process Standard (1)(E)

 Problem 1 **Got It?** Using a Net to Find Total Surface Area of a Prism

Learning Animation

What is the total surface area of the triangular prism? Use a net.

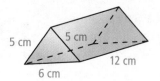

5 cm

5 cm

6 cm

12 cm

TEKS Process Standard (1)(G)

 Problem 2 **Got It?** Using Formulas to Find Total Surface Area of a Prism

Learning Animation

a. What is the lateral area of the prism at the right?

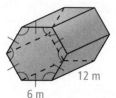

12 m

6 m

b. What is the area of a base in simplest radical form?

c. What is the total surface area of the prism rounded to a whole number?

ELPS Read the Got It with a classmate. Use the diagram to answer the following questions: What shape are the lateral faces of the prism? How many lateral faces are there? What shape are the bases? How many bases are there? Work together to find the area of one of the lateral faces and the area of the base.

Lesson 14-2 | Surface Areas of Prisms and Cylinders

Problem 3 | **Got It?** | Finding Total Surface Area of a Cylinder

A cylinder has a height of 9 cm and a radius of 10 cm. What is the total surface area of the cylinder in terms of π?

 Learning Animation

 Problem 4 | **Got It?** | Applying Area of a Cylinder

In Problem 4, you found the lateral area of a cylindrical stencil roller with height 6 in. and diameter 2.5 in. is about 47.1 in.^{2}.

 Learning Animation

a. A smaller stencil roller has a height of 1.5 in. and the same diameter as the larger roller. What area does the smaller roller cover in one turn? Round your answer to the nearest tenth.

b. What is the ratio of the smaller roller's height to the larger roller's height? What is the ratio of the areas the rollers can cover in one turn (smaller to larger)?

Lesson Check

Do you know HOW?

1. What is the total surface area of each solid?

a.

5 in.

4 in.

5 in.

b.

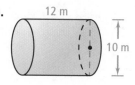

12 m

10 m

Math Tools

Online Practice

Virtual Nerd Tutorials

2. The total surface area of the prism at the right is 336 square centimeters. What is the height of the prism?

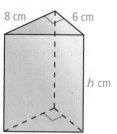

8 cm   6 cm

h cm

3. A 5-ft long lead pipe has a diameter of 4 in. The diameter of the hole through the center of the pipe is 3 in. What is the total surface area of the pipe in terms of π? (*Hint:* The surface area includes the inside, the outside, and the edges at the ends of the pipe.)

Lesson Check

Do you UNDERSTAND?

4. **Vocabulary** Name the lateral faces and the bases of the prism at the right.

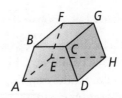

5. **Evaluate Reasonableness (1)(B)** Your friend drew a net of a cylinder. What is your friend's error? Explain.

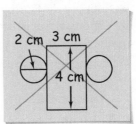

6. **Analyze Mathematical Relationships (1)(F)** What is the relationship between the total surface area of a triangular prism and the total surface area of a second triangular prism whose corresponding faces are similar polygons with a scale factor of 2? Explain.

TEXAS Test Practice

Multiple Choice

For Exercises 1–6, choose the correct letter.

1. For his birthday, you buy your dad a package of tennis balls that come in a cylindrical container with diameter 6.9 cm and height 20.6 cm. You cover the container in wrapping paper before giving it to him. What is the area of the wrapping paper? Assume there is no overlap. Round to the nearest whole number.

   A. 447 cm^2 **B.** 521 cm^2 **C.** 1192 cm^2 **D.** 3111 cm^2

For Exercises 2 and 3, use the prism at the right.

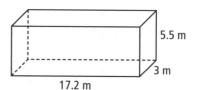

2. What is the total surface area of the prism?

   F. 283.8 m^2 **H.** 325.4 m^2

   G. 292.4 m^2 **J.** 407 m^2

3. Suppose the 3 m-by-17.2 m faces are the bases of the prism. What are the dimensions of a rectangular prism with the same lateral area as the prism in the diagram?

   A. length = 12.9 m   **C.** length = 6.2 m
   width = 4 m   width = 9.6 m
   height = 5.5 m   height = 9.9 m

   B. length = 4.6 m   **D.** length = 8.6 m
   width = 5.5 m   width = 6 m
   height = 11 m   height = 5.5 m

For Exercises 4 and 5, use the cylinder at the right.

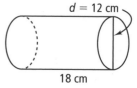

4. A company sells olives in a large can as shown at right. The label wraps around the entire lateral surface of the can. What is the area of the label?

   F. 12π cm^2 **H.** 216π cm^2

   G. 18π cm^2 **J.** 288π cm^2

5. The can is made from aluminum. How much aluminum will be needed to make the total surface of the can?

   A. 12π cm^2 **B.** 18π cm^2 **C.** 216π cm^2 **D.** 288π cm^2

6. The height of a cylinder is three times the diameter of the base. The total surface area of the cylinder is 126π ft^2. What is the radius of the base?

   F. 3 ft   **G.** 6 ft   **H.** 9 ft   **J.** 18 ft

Short Response

7. What are the lateral area and the total surface area of the prism?

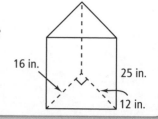

Lesson 14-2 | Surface Areas of Prisms and Cylinders

You are building a model of a clock tower. You have already constructed the basic structure of the tower as shown. Now you want to paint the roof. How much area does the paint need to cover? Give your answer in square inches. Explain your method.

Interactive Exploration

Vocabulary Online

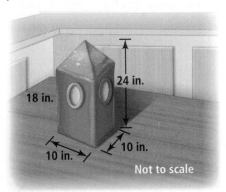
18 in.
24 in.
10 in.
10 in.
Not to scale

 Connect Mathematical Ideas (1)(F) How does this problem relate to a problem you have seen before?

Problem 1 | **Got It?** | Finding the Total Surface Area of a Pyramid

a. A square pyramid has base edges of 5 m and a slant height of 3 m. What is the total surface area of the pyramid?

b. Suppose the slant height of a pyramid is doubled. How does this affect the lateral area of the pyramid? Explain.

Learning Animation

TEKS Process Standard (1)(G)

 Problem 2 | **Got It?** | Finding the Lateral Area of a Pyramid

a. What is the lateral area of the hexagonal pyramid shown? Round to the nearest square foot.

42 ft

$18\sqrt{3}$ ft

36 ft

Learning Animation

b. How does the slant height of a regular pyramid relate to its height? Explain.

 Problem 3 | **Got It?** | Finding the Total Surface Area of a Cone

The radius of the base of a cone is 16 m. Its slant height is 28 m. What is the total surface area in terms of π?

Learning Animation

ELPS Read the Got It with a classmate. Summarize the information given by drawing and labeling a cone. Point out the base, the lateral surface, and the slant height. Then listen as your partner summarizes the process needed to find the total surface area.

Lesson 14-3 | Surface Areas of Pyramids and Cones

Problem 4 **Got It?** Finding the Lateral Area of a Cone

Learning
Animation

a. What is the lateral area of a traffic cone with radius 10 in. and height 28 in.?
Round to the nearest whole number.

b. Suppose the radius of a cone is halved, but the slant height remains the same.
How does this affect the lateral area of the cone? Explain.

 Problem 5 **Got It?** Finding the Surface Area of a Three-
Dimensional Composite Figure

Learning
Animation

A company packages pencils in a cardboard container that is composed of a
cylinder and two right cones, as shown. The containers are made from sheets of
cardboard with an area of 10,000 cm². Assuming 10% of each sheet of cardboard is
waste, how many containers can be made from a sheet of cardboard?

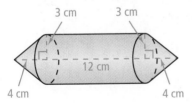

3 cm   3 cm

12 cm

4 cm   4 cm

Do you know HOW?

1. Find the lateral area and the total surface area of each solid.

a.
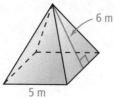
6 m

5 m

b.
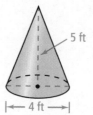
5 ft

|← 4 ft →|

Math Tools

Online Practice

Virtual Nerd Tutorials

2. The lateral area of the square pyramid shown at the right is 118 cm². The total surface area is 182 cm². What is the length of a side (s) of the base, the slant height (ℓ), and the height (h)?

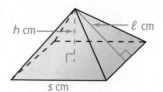
h cm — ℓ cm

s cm

3. On a coordinate grid, a polygon with vertices (0, 0), (4, 3), (7, 3), and (7, 0) is rotated around the x-axis to generate a three-dimensional object. What is the total surface area of the composite figure? If necessary, round to the nearest tenth.

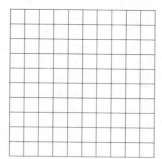

Lesson Check

Do you UNDERSTAND?

4. **Vocabulary** How do the height and slant height of a pyramid differ?

Math Tools

Online Practice

Virtual Nerd Tutorials

5. **Analyze Mathematical Relationships (1)(F)** How are the formulas for the total surface area of a prism and the total surface area of a pyramid alike? How are they different?

6. **Explain Mathematical Ideas (1)(G)** A cone has height 7 and radius 3. Your classmate calculates its lateral area. What is your classmate's error? Explain.

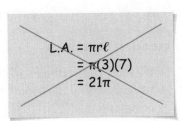

$$L.A. = \pi r \ell$$
$$= \pi(3)(7)$$
$$= 21\pi$$

Lesson 14-3 │ **Surface Areas of Pyramids and Cones**

TEXAS Test Practice

Multiple Choice

For Exercises 1–5, choose the correct letter.

1. A camping tent in the shape of a regular pentagonal pyramid has a height of 5 ft. The area of the base is 62 ft². What is the total surface area of the tent? Round to the nearest square foot.

   A. 98 ft²　　　　**B.** 137 ft²　　　　**C.** 159 ft²　　　　**D.** 217 ft²

2. What is the lateral surface area of a cone with radius 11 cm and slant height 19 cm?

   F. 19π cm²　　　**G.** 30π cm²　　　**H.** 200π cm²　　　**J.** 209π cm²

3. What is the lateral area of the square pyramid, to the nearest square meter?

   A. 165 m²

   B. 176 m²

   C. 330 m²

   D. 351 m²

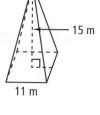
15 m
11 m

4. What is the total surface area of the cone, to the nearest square centimeter?

   F. 221 cm²

   G. 240 cm²

   H. 304 cm²

   J. 620 cm²

12.5 cm
9 cm

5. Six cups of batter will make 212.8 in.² of waffle cones. The waffle cones are 6 in. tall and have a diameter of $2\frac{3}{4}$ in. Assume the amount of waffle needed for each cone is equal to the cone's lateral area. How many waffle cones can you make with 6 cups of batter?

   A. 3　　　　　**B.** 7　　　　　**C.** 8　　　　　**D.** 9

Extended Response

6. What are the perimeter of the base, slant height, lateral area, and surface area for the square pyramid, to the nearest tenth of a meter or square meter?

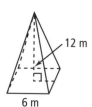
12 m
6 m

SOLVE IT!

A 1 cm-by-1 cm-by-1 cm cube is shown below at the left. How many of these cubes can you fit in each box? Explain your reasoning.

Interactive
Exploration

Vocabulary
Online

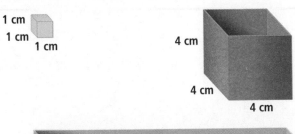

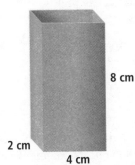

1 cm
1 cm
1 cm

4 cm

4 cm

4 cm

8 cm

2 cm

4 cm

2 cm

2 cm

16 cm

Use a Problem-Solving Model (1)(B) Evaluate your problem-solving model. Which parts were helpful? Which would you want to revise? Explain.

Problem 1 | Got It? | Finding the Volume of a Rectangular Prism

a. What is the volume of the rectangular prism shown?

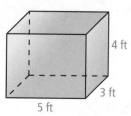

4 ft

3 ft

5 ft

Learning
Animation

b. Suppose the prism is turned so that the base is 4 ft by 5 ft and the height is 3 ft. Does the volume change? Explain.

TEKS Process Standard (1)(E)

Problem 2 | Got It? | Finding the Volume of a Triangular Prism

a. What is the volume of the triangular prism shown?

10 m

6 m

5 m

Learning
Animation

b. Suppose the height of a prism is doubled. How does this affect the volume of the prism? Explain.

Problem 3 | **Got It?** | Finding the Volume of a Cylinder

a. What is the volume of the cylinder in terms of π?

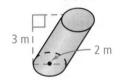

3 m

2 m

Learning
Animation

b. Suppose the radius of a cylinder is halved. How does this affect the volume of the cylinder? Explain.

TEKS Process Standard (1)(G)

 Problem 4 | **Got It?** | Finding the Volume of a Composite Figure

What is the approximate volume of the lunch box shown? Round to the nearest cubic inch.

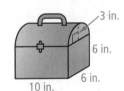

3 in.

6 in.

6 in.

10 in.

Learning
Animation

ELPS Discuss with a classmate any ideas you have to solve the Got It. Can the lunch box be divided into other three-dimensional shapes that may be easier to work with? Together, make a plan to find the volume.

Lesson 14-4 | Volumes of Prisms and Cylinders

475

Lesson Check

Do you know HOW?

Math Tools

Online Practice

Virtual Nerd Tutorials

1. What is the volume of each figure? If necessary, round to the nearest whole number.

   a.

   3 ft
   3 ft
   6 ft

   b.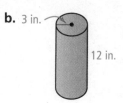
   3 in.
   12 in.

2. A rectangle with vertices $(0, 2)$, $(7, 2)$, $(0, 4)$ and $(7, 4)$ on the coordinate plane is rotated around the line $y = 2$. What is the volume of the three-dimensional solid generated? If necessary, round to the nearest whole number.

   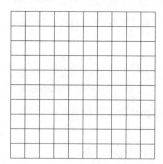

3. Use the diagram of the backpack at the right.

   a. What two figures approximate the shape of the backpack?

   17 in.
   4 in.
   12 in.

   b. What is the volume of the backpack in terms of π?

   c. What is the volume of the backpack to the nearest cubic inch?

Lesson 14-4 | Volumes of Prisms and Cylinders

476

Lesson Check

Do you UNDERSTAND?

4. **Vocabulary** Is the figure at the right a composite space figure? Explain your reasoning.

Math Tools

Online Practice

Virtual Nerd Tutorials

5. **Analyze Mathematical Relationships (1)(F)** How are the formulas for the volume of a prism and the volume of a cylinder alike? How are they different?

6. **Justify Mathematical Arguments (1)(G)** How is the volume of a rectangular prism with base 2 m-by-3 m and height 4 m related to the volume of a rectangular prism with base 3 m-by-4 m and height 2 m? Explain.

TEXAS Test Practice

Gridded Response

Solve each exercise and enter your answer on the grid provided.

1. A box of index cards is shown in the diagram at the right. What is the volume in cubic inches of the box?

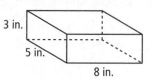

3 in.
5 in.
8 in.

2. A tunnel at the playground is in the shape of a triangular prism, as shown in the diagram at the right. What is the volume of the tunnel to the nearest cubic foot?

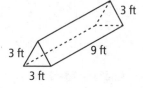

3 ft
3 ft
9 ft
3 ft

3. What is x, if the volume of the cylinder is 768π cm^3?

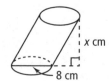

x cm
8 cm

4. What is the volume in cubic inches of the solid figure, rounded to the nearest cubic inch?

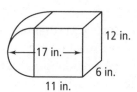

12 in.
17 in.
6 in.
11 in.

1. **2.** **3.** **4.**

Lesson 14-4 | Volumes of Prisms and Cylinders

478

SOLVE IT!

Look for a pattern in the volumes of the prism and pyramid pairs below. Use the pattern to find the volume of a pyramid with a base 2 ft-by-3 ft and height 5 ft. Explain your reasoning.

Interactive Exploration

Vocabulary Online

1 ft
1 ft
1 ft

Pyramid volume $= \frac{1}{3}$ ft^3

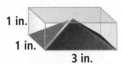

1 in.
1 in.
3 in.
Pyramid volume = 1 in.^{3}

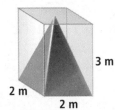

3 m
2 m
2 m
Pyramid volume = 4 m^3

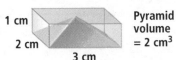

1 cm
2 cm
3 cm

Pyramid volume = 2 cm^3

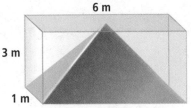

6 m
3 m
1 m
Pyramid volume = 6 m^3

Not to scale

Analyze Mathematical Relationships (1)(F) What mathematical relationships did you identify in the problem? How did you use them to solve the problem?

Problem 1 | **Got It?** | **Finding the Volume of a Pyramid**

A sports arena shaped like a pyramid has a base area of about 300,000 ft² and a height of 321 ft. What is the approximate volume of the arena?

Learning Animation

TEKS Process Standard (1)(D)

 Problem 2 | **Got It?** | **Finding the Volume of a Pyramid**

What is the volume of a square pyramid with base edges 24 m and slant height 13 m?

Learning Animation

Lesson 14-5 | Volumes of Pyramids and Cones

480

Problem 3 | **Got It?** | **Finding the Volume of a Cone**

Learning Animation

a. The tepee in Problem 3 is 12 ft high with a base diameter of 14 ft. The height and radius of a child's tepee are half those of the tepee in Problem 3. What is the volume of the child's tepee to the nearest cubic foot?

b. In Problem 3, the volume of the original tepee was approximately 616 ft³. What is the relationship between the volume of the original tepee and the child's tepee?

 ELPS Listen as your partner summarizes the Got It. Ask questions to make sure you understand the problem. Discuss the meanings of any unfamiliar terms. Then explain the way you would solve the problem. Answer any questions your partner may have about your proposed method.

TEKS Process Standard (1)(E)

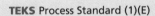

 Problem 4 | **Got It?** | **Finding the Volume of an Oblique Cone**

Learning Animation

a. What is the volume of the oblique cone at the right in terms of π? What is the volume rounded to the nearest cubic meter?

12 m

6 m

b. How does the volume of an oblique cone compare to the volume of a right cone with the same diameter and height? Explain.

Lesson Check

Do you know HOW?

1. What is the volume of each figure? If necessary, round to the nearest tenth.

a.

8 in.

6 in.

6 in.

b.
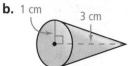

1 cm   3 cm

Math Tools

Online Practice

Virtual Nerd Tutorials

2. The volume of a square pyramid with height 15 ft is 1280 ft³. What is the slant height of the pyramid?

3. The volume of a cone with a base diameter of 10 cm is 100π cm³. What is the total surface area of the cone in terms of π?

Do you UNDERSTAND?

4. Analyze Mathematical Relationships (1)(F) How are the formulas for the volume of a pyramid and the volume of a cone alike? How are they different?

5. Explain Mathematical Ideas (1)(G) A square pyramid has base edges 13 ft and height 10 ft. A cone has diameter 13 ft and height 10 ft. Your friend claims that the figures have the same volume because the volume formulas for a pyramid and a cone are the same: $V = \frac{1}{3}Bh$. What is her error?

6. Evaluate Reasonableness (1)(B) A cone and a cylinder have the same height and equal volumes. What is the ratio of the radius of the cylinder to the radius of the cone? Explain how you found the ratio and how you know your answer is reasonable.

TEXAS Test Practice

Multiple Choice

For Exercises 1–5, choose the correct letter.

1. Refer to the pyramid at the right. Which of the following is not true?

   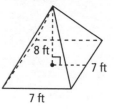

   A. The surface area of the pyramid is 171 ft².
   B. The volume of the pyramid is $130\frac{2}{3}$ ft³.
   C. The lateral area of the pyramid is 122 ft².
   D. none of these

2. What is the volume of the cone, rounded to the nearest cubic inch?

   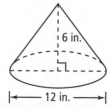

   F. 72 in.³
   G. 226 in.³
   H. 905 in.³
   J. 2714 in.³

3. A salt shaker is shaped like a cube with a square pyramid on top. The length of each side of the cube is 3 cm. The height of the square pyramid is 2 cm. How many cubic centimeters of salt can the salt shaker hold?

   A. 15 cm³   **C.** 45 cm³
   B. 33 cm³   **D.** 54 cm³

4. What is the value of x, if the volume of the cone is 12π m³?

   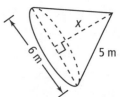

   F. 4 m   **H.** 6 m
   G. 5 m   **J.** 10 m

5. What is the diameter of an oblique cone with height 8 m and volume 150π m³?

   A. 7.5 m   **C.** $7.5\sqrt{3}$ m
   B. $5\sqrt{3}$ m   **D.** 15 m

Short Response

6. A student calculates the volume of the given cone as approximately 2094 cm³. Explain the error in the student's reasoning and find the actual volume of the cone. Round to the nearest cubic centimeter.

   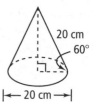

SOLVE IT!

The three orange slices below were cut from three different oranges. Do you have sufficient information to tell which orange is the largest? If not, explain what information you would need.

Interactive Exploration

Vocabulary Online

7 cm

A

4 cm

B

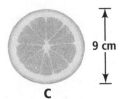

9 cm

C

 Apply Mathematics (1)(A) Describe another real-world situation for which you could apply the same mathematical model.

Problem 1 **Got It?** **Finding the Surface Area of a Sphere**

What is the surface area of a sphere with a diameter of 14 in.? Give your answer in terms of π and rounded to the nearest square inch.

Learning Animation

 ELPS Read the Got It with a classmate. Discuss the following questions: What is the formula for finding the surface area of a sphere? What is the radius of this sphere? Calculate the answer and compare your results with other students in the class.

TEKS Process Standard (1)(C)

 Problem 2 **Got It?** **Finding Surface Area**

What is the surface area of a melon with circumference 18 in.? Round your answer to the nearest ten square inches.

Learning Animation

Problem 3 | **Got It?** | **Finding the Volume of a Sphere**

Learning
Animation

a. A sphere has a diameter of 60 in. What is its volume to the nearest cubic inch?

b. Suppose the radius of a sphere is halved. How does this affect the volume of the sphere? Explain.

TEKS Process Standard (1)(D)

 Problem 4 | **Got It?** | **Finding the Volume of a Composite Figure**

Learning
Animation

An aquarium consists of two identical rectangular prisms that are connected by a cylinder, as shown. If 1 gallon equals 231 cubic inches, how many gallons of water does the aquarium hold? Round to the nearest tenth of a gallon.

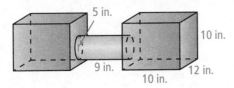

 Problem 5 | **Got It?** | **Using Volume to Find Surface Area**

Learning
Animation

The volume of a sphere is 4200 ft^3. What is its surface area to the nearest tenth of a square foot?

Lesson Check

Do you know HOW?

1. The diameter of a sphere is 12 ft.

   a. What is its surface area in terms of π?

Online
Practice

   b. What is its volume to the nearest tenth of a cubic foot?

Virtual Nerd
Tutorials

2. A sphere has the same volume as a cylinder with radius 10 cm and height $1\frac{2}{3}$ cm. What is the surface area of the sphere in terms of π?

3. Find the only possible radius for which the volume and surface area of a sphere are numerically equal.

Lesson Check

Do you UNDERSTAND?

Math Tools

4. **Vocabulary** What is the ratio of the area of a great circle to the surface area of the sphere?

Online Practice

Virtual Nerd Tutorials

5. **Analyze Mathematical Relationships (1)(F)** Your classmate claims that if you double the radius of a sphere, its surface area and volume will quadruple. What is your classmate's error? Explain.

6. **Create Representations to Communicate Mathematical Ideas (1)(E)**
   A sphere fits inside a cylinder so that it touches both the sides and the top and bottom of the cylinder. What must be true about the relationship between the radius of the sphere and the height of the cylinder? Draw and label a sketch to justify your answer.

TEXAS Test Practice

Multiple Choice

For Exercises 1–5, choose the correct letter.

1. Attempting to break a world record, you construct a rubber band ball with a diameter of 6 ft. What is the approximate volume of your rubber band ball?

   A. 113 ft^3 **C.** 216 ft^3

   B. 452 ft^3 **D.** 904 ft^3

2. What is the approximate surface area of the sphere?

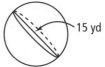

   F. 225 yd^2 **H.** 1767 yd^2

   G. 707 yd^2 **J.** 5301 yd^2

3. The manager of a basketball factory found that the surface area of an inflated basketball is approximately 286.46 in.^{2}. The factory ships the balls flat. If you buy one of these basketballs, approximately how many cubic inches of air will you need to pump into it? Note: Ignore the thickness of the ball.

   A. 456 in.^{3} **B.** 573 in.^{3} **C.** 912 in.^{3} **D.** 1126 in.^{3}

4. What is the approximate surface area of the sphere?

   F. 342.3 km^2 **H.** 903.4 km^2

   G. 451.9 km^2 **J.** 2713 km^2

5. A spherical water tank is being constructed with an internal capacity of $523\frac{1}{3}$ ft^3. The tank will be constructed out of concrete and its outer wall will be 6 in. thick. What volume of concrete will be needed to construct the water tank? Round to the nearest tenth.

   $C = 37.68$ km

   A. 6 ft^3 **B.** 173.2 ft^3 **C.** 523.3 ft^3 **D.** 696.6 ft^3

Short Response

6. Suppose a wealthy entrepreneur commissions the design of a spherical spaceship to house a small group for a week in orbit around the Earth. The designer allocates 1000 ft^3 for each person, plus an additional 4073.5 ft^3 for various necessary machines. The diameter of the ship is 26.8 ft.

   a. What is the volume of the spaceship?

   b. For approximately how many people is the ship designed?

SOLVE IT!

A baker is making a three-layer wedding cake. Each layer has a square base. Each dimension of the middle layer is $\frac{1}{2}$ the corresponding dimension of the bottom layer. Each dimension of the top layer is $\frac{1}{2}$ the corresponding dimension of the middle layer. What conjecture can you make about the relationship between the volumes of the layers? Calculate the volumes to check your answer. Modify your conjecture if necessary.

Interactive Exploration

Vocabulary Online

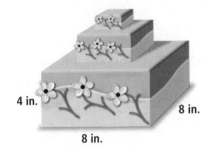

4 in.

8 in.

8 in.

 Explain Mathematical Ideas (1)(G) A classmate questions your solution to the problem. Use precise mathematical language to explain why your solution is correct.

Problem 1 | **Got It?** | Analyzing Proportional Change in Dimensions of a Three-Dimensional Figure

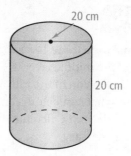

a. How is the surface area of the cylinder affected if all dimensions of the cylinder are multiplied by 0.5? By 3?

20 cm

20 cm

Learning Animation

b. How is the volume of the cylinder affected if all dimensions of the cylinder are multiplied by 0.5? By 3?

TEKS Process Standard (1)(F)

 Problem 2 | **Got It?** | Identifying Similar Solids

Are the two cylinders similar? If so, what is the scale factor of the first figure to the second figure?

Learning Animation

 6 12   5 10

Problem 3 | **Got It?** | **Finding the Scale Factor**

Learning
Animation

a. What is the scale factor of two similar prisms with surface areas 144 m^2 and 324 m^2?

b. Are any two square prisms similar? Explain.

TEKS Process Standard (1)(G)

 Problem 4 | **Got It?** | **Using a Scale Factor**

The volumes of two similar solids are 128 m³ and 250 m³. The surface area of the larger solid is 250 m². What is the surface area of the smaller solid?

Learning
Animation

ELPS Discuss the following questions with a classmate. If the scale factor of two similar solids is $a : b$, what is the ratio of the volumes in terms of a and b? What is the ratio in this problem? Set these two ratios equal to each other. Then repeat the same process for the surface areas.

Lesson 14-7 │ **Surface Areas and Volumes of Related Solids**

494

Problem 5 [**Got It?**] **Using a Scale Factor to Find Capacity**

A marble paperweight shaped like a pyramid weighs 0.15 lb. How much does a similarly shaped marble paperweight weigh if each dimension is three times as large?

Learning
Animation

 Problem 6 [**Got It?**] **Analyzing Non-Proportional Change in Dimensions of a Three-Dimensional Figure**

a. How is the surface area of the rectangular prism affected if the length and width of the prism are doubled and the height is multiplied by 1.5?

Learning
Animation

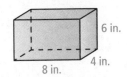
6 in.
4 in.
8 in.

b. How is the volume of the rectangular prism affected if the length and width of the prism are doubled and the height is multiplied by 1.5?

Lesson Check

Do you know HOW?

1. Which two of the following cones are similar? What is their scale factor?

30 m	35 m	45 m
20 m	25 m	30 m
Cone 1	**Cone 2**	**Cone 3**

Math Tools

Online Practice

Virtual Nerd Tutorials

2. The volumes of two similar containers are 115 in.^{3} and 67 in.^{3}. The surface area of the smaller container is 108 in.^{2}. What is the surface area of the larger container?

3. A cylinder with a 4-in. diameter and a 6-in. height holds 1 lb of oatmeal. To the nearest ounce, how much oatmeal will a similar 10-in.-high cylinder hold? (*Hint:* 1 lb = 16 oz)

Math
Tools

Online
Practice

Virtual Nerd
Tutorials

Lesson Check

Do you UNDERSTAND?

4. Vocabulary How are similar solids different from similar polygons? Explain.

5. Evaluate Reasonableness (1)(B) Two cubes have surface areas 49 cm^2 and 64 cm^2. Your classmate tried to find the scale factor of the larger cube to the smaller cube. Explain why your classmate's answer is not reasonable and correct her error.

$$\frac{a^2}{b^2} = \frac{49}{64}$$

$$\frac{a}{b} = \frac{7}{8}$$

The scale factor of the larger cube to the smaller cube is 7 : 8.

6. Analyze Mathematical Relationships (1)(F) Two similar prisms have heights x and y.

  a. What is their scale factor?

  b. What is the ratio of their surface areas?

  c. What is the ratio of their volumes?

Multiple Choice

For Exercises 1–5, choose the correct letter.

1. For the school play, you create a scale model of the Great Pyramid of Giza. The scale factor of your model to the actual pyramid is 1 ft : 10 m. The lateral surface area of the Great Pyramid is approximately 85,900 m². About how much plywood will you need to cover the lateral faces of your model?

   A. 85.9 ft²   **B.** 859 ft²   **C.** 8590 ft²   **D.** 8,590,000 ft²

2. Which pair of figures below is similar?

   F.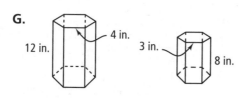

   H.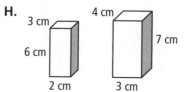

   G.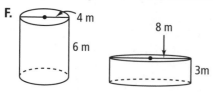

   J.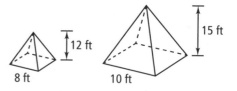

3. What is the ratio of the surface areas of the similar square pyramids at the right?

   A. 4 : 5
   B. 8 : 10
   C. 16 : 25
   D. 64 : 125

   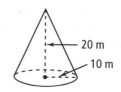

4. A large can of tomato sauce is similar to a small can of tomato sauce. The radius of the large can is 7.5 cm. The radius of the small can is 3 cm. What is the ratio of the volume of the small can to the volume of the large can?

   F. 3 : 7.5   **G.** 9 : 22.5   **H.** 9 : 56.25   **J.** 8 : 125

5. The surface areas of two similar prisms are 132 m² and 297 m². The volume of the smaller prism is 264 m³. What is the volume of the larger prism?

   A. 594 m³   **B.** 891 m³   **C.** 1336.5 m³   **D.** 3007.125 m³

Short Response

6. A medium-sized box can hold 55 T-shirts. If the dimensions of a jumbo box are three times that of the medium box, how many T-shirts can the jumbo box hold? Explain.

SOLVE IT!

You find an old clock in your attic. The hour hand of the clock is broken off. Between 12:00 and 2:00, how many positions are possible for the hour hand? For a 12-hour period, how many positions are possible for the hour hand? What is the probability that the clock stopped some time between 12:00 and 2:00?

Interactive Exploration

Vocabulary Online

 Use Multiple Representations to Communicate Mathematical Ideas (1)(D)
What is another representation you could use to present your solution?
Explain how the representation communicates the same information.

Problem 1 Got It? Calculating Experimental Probability

A park has 538 trees. You choose 40 at random and determine that 25 are maple trees. What is the experimental probability that a tree chosen at random is a maple tree? About how many trees in the park are likely to be maple trees?

Learning
Animation

TEKS Process Standard (1)(E)

Problem 2 Got It? Calculating Theoretical Probability

What is the probability of getting each sum when rolling two standard number cubes?

a. 9

b. 2

c. 13

ELPS Discuss with a classmate. What pattern do you notice when listing the number combinations that add up to a particular number? How many combinations add up to 9? What is the probability of rolling a sum of 9? A sum of 2? Be sure to use key vocabulary words and expressions such as *sum, combination, likelihood, probability,* and *theoretical probability*. After discussing, switch partners and explain your thinking for determining the probability of rolling a given sum. Be sure to use key vocabulary words and expressions.

Problem 3 | **Got It?** | Using Probabilities of Events and Their Complements

Learning Animation

A jar contains 10 red marbles, 8 green marbles, 5 blue marbles, and 6 white marbles. What is the probability that a randomly chosen marble is not red?

Lesson Check

Do you know HOW?

1. Use the spinner to find P(an even number) and P(a number greater than 5).

Math Tools

Online Practice

Virtual Nerd Tutorials

2. A bag contains 12 marbles. Each marble is green, blue, or red. The probability that a randomly selected marble is green is $\frac{1}{3}$. The probability that a randomly selected marble is blue is $\frac{1}{2}$. How many of each color marble are in the bag?

3. A student randomly selects a card from a set of ten cards numbered from 1 to 10. She notes the number on the card and places it back in the deck. She repeats this 20 times and finds that she chose a prime number 6 times. Explain how the student's experimental probability of choosing a prime number compares to the theoretical probability of choosing a prime number.

Lesson Check

Do you UNDERSTAND?

Math Tools

Online Practice

Virtual Nerd Tutorials

4. **Vocabulary** How are experimental and theoretical probability similar? How are they different?

5. **Explain Mathematical Ideas (1)(G)** Your friend says that the probability of rolling a number less than 7 on a standard number cube is 100. Do you agree? If so, why? If not, explain your friend's error and find the correct probability.

6. **Justify Mathematical Arguments (1)(G)** When you roll a standard number cube, is it possible for an event to have a probability of $\frac{1}{8}$? Justify your response using precise mathematical language.

Lesson 15-1 | **Experimental and Theoretical Probability**

503

TEXAS Test Practice

Multiple Choice

For Exercises 1–5, choose the correct letter.

1. What is the probability of rolling an even product when rolling two number cubes?

   A. $\frac{1}{4}$ **C.** $\frac{1}{2}$

   B. $\frac{1}{3}$ **D.** $\frac{3}{4}$

2. A coin is tossed 30 times and lands on heads 17 times. What is the experimental probability of the coin landing on tails?

   F. $\frac{17}{30}$ **H.** $\frac{13}{30}$

   G. $\frac{1}{2}$ **J.** $\frac{8}{15}$

3. What is the theoretical probability of randomly choosing a science book from a shelf that holds 3 mystery books, 5 science books, and 4 nature books?

   A. $\frac{1}{4}$ **C.** $\frac{5}{12}$

   B. $\frac{1}{3}$ **D.** $\frac{7}{12}$

4. What is the complement of rolling a 2 or 5 on a number cube?

   F. rolling a 5 or a 2   **H.** rolling a 1, 3, 4, or 5

   G. rolling a 1, 3, 4, or 6   **J.** rolling a 3

5. In a certain video game, chests contain either money or a potion. You look in 10 chests and find money in 8 of them. You need to find 5 more potions. Based on the experimental probability of finding money, how many more chests do you expect you will need to open?

   A. 5   **C.** 30

   B. 25   **D.** 50

Short Response

6. A spinner has four equal sections labeled 2, 4, 6, and 8. Suppose you spin the spinner twice. What is the theoretical probability that the sum of the outcomes is 10? Show the favorable outcomes.

Scan page for an interactive
version of this Solve It.

SOLVE IT!

A fair coin is equally likely to land heads up or tails up. Suppose you toss a fair coin three times. What is the probability that the coin will land tails up exactly twice? Explain your reasoning.

Interactive Exploration

Vocabulary Online

Toss 1   **Toss 2**   **Toss 3**

Explain Mathematical Ideas (1)(G) A classmate questions your solution to the problem. Use precise mathematical language to explain why your solution is correct.

Problem 1 | **Got It?** | **Using Segments to Find Probability**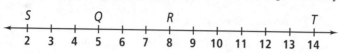

Point H on $\overline{ST}$ is selected at random. What is the probability that H lies on $\overline{SR}$?

```
S       Q         R             T
2  3  4  5  6  7  8  9  10 11 12 13 14
```

TEKS Process Standard (1)(E)

 Problem 2 | **Got It?** | **Using Segments to Find Probability**

A commuter train runs every 25 min. If a commuter arrives at the station at a random time, what is the probability that the commuter will have to wait no more than 5 min for the train?

TEKS Process Standard (1)(B)

 Problem 3 | **Got It?** | **Using Area to Find Probability**

A triangle is inscribed in a square. Point *T* in the square is selected at random. What is the probability that *T* lies in the shaded region?

 5 in.

 Learning Animation

ELPS With a classmate, make a list of questions that need to be answered in order to solve the Got It. Then discuss your questions with another pair. Work together to answer the questions and find the probability that *T* lies in the shaded region.

 Problem 4 | **Got It?** | **Using Area to Find Probability**

Learning Animation

Refer to the picture in Problem 4.

a. An archery target has 5 colored scoring zones formed by concentric circles. The target's diameter is 122 cm. The radius of the yellow zone is 12.2 cm. The width of each of the other zones is also 12.2 cm. If an arrow hits the target at a random point, what is the probability that it hits the yellow zone?

b. If an arrow hits the target at a random point, is it more likely to hit the black zone or the red zone? Explain.

Lesson Check

Do you know HOW?

1. Point T on $\overline{AD}$ is chosen at random. What is the probability that T lies on the given segment?

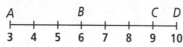

a. $\overline{AC}$ b. $\overline{BC}$

Math Tools

Online Practice

Virtual Nerd Tutorials

2. A point K in the regular hexagon is chosen at random. What is the probability that K lies in the region that is *not* shaded?

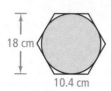

18 cm

10.4 cm

3. A friend is preparing a target for a beanbag toss by cutting two congruent squares from a rectangular piece of wood, as shown. Your friend assumes that beanbags will land on the target at random and wants the probability that a beanbag lands in one of the squares to be 30%. What should be the length s of the sides of the squares?

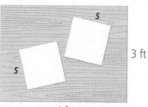

s

3 ft

s

4 ft

Lesson Check

Do you UNDERSTAND?

Math
Tools

Online
Practice

Virtual Nerd
Tutorials

4. **Vocabulary** How is calculating a geometric probability similar to and different from theoretical probability?

5. **Analyze Mathematical Relationships (1)(F)** In the figure, $\frac{SQ}{QT} = \frac{1}{2}$. What is the probability that a point on $\overline{ST}$ chosen at random will lie on $\overline{QT}$? Explain.

6. **Explain Mathematical Ideas (1)(G)** Your class needs to find the probability that a point A in the square chosen at random lies in the shaded region. Your classmate's work is shown below. What is the error? Explain.

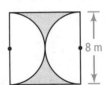
8 m

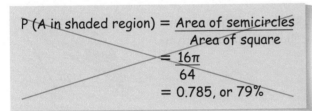

P (A in shaded region) = Area of semicircles
                          Area of square

= 16π
  64

= 0.785, or 79%

TEXAS Test Practice

Multiple Choice

For Exercises 1–4, choose the correct letter.

1. You have a 7-cm straw and a 10-cm straw. You want to cut the 10-cm straw into two pieces so that the three pieces make a triangle. If you cut the straw at a random point, what is the probability that you can make a triangle?

A. 30% **B.** 40% **C.** 60% **D.** 70%

2. Point P on $\overline{AD}$ is chosen at random. For which of the figures below is the probability that P is on $\overline{BC}$ 25%? Note: Diagrams not drawn to scale.

F.
```
   2        5        8       10
   ├────────┼────────┼────────┤
   A        B        C        D
```

G.
```
   1        2        3        4
   ├────────┼────────┼────────┤
   A        B        C        D
```

H.
```
   2        3        4        5
   ├────────┼────────┼────────┤
   A        B        C        D
```

J.
```
   1        2        3        5
   ├────────┼────────┼────────┤
   A        B        C        D
```

3. Point P is chosen at random in a circle. If a square is inscribed in the circle, what is the probability that P lies outside the square?

A. $1 - \dfrac{1}{2\pi}$ **B.** $1 - \dfrac{2}{\pi}$ **C.** $1 - \dfrac{\pi}{2}$ **D.** $1 - \dfrac{1}{4\pi}$

4. Point X on $\overline{QT}$ is chosen at random. What is the probability that X is on $\overline{ST}$?

F. $\dfrac{QT}{ST}$ **G.** $\dfrac{ST}{QT}$ **H.** $\dfrac{QS}{ST}$ **J.** $\dfrac{ST}{QS}$

Short Response

5. Point P is chosen at random in $\odot S$. What is the probability that P lies in the shaded segment shown in the diagram at the right? Show your work.

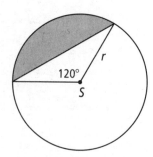

In Chemistry class, you and your lab partner must add the samples in the test tubes to a mixture. The reactions that occur depend on the order in which you add them. How many different ways can you add the samples to the mixture?

Interactive Exploration

Vocabulary Online

Use Multiple Representations to Communicate Mathematical Ideas (1)(D)
What is another representation you could use to solve the problem? Explain why the representation would be useful.

Problem 1 **Got It?** Using the Fundamental Counting Principle

Suppose that a computer generates passwords that begin with a letter followed by 2 digits, such as R38. The same digit can be used more than once. How many different passwords can the computer generate?

 Learning Animation

 Problem 2 **Got It?** Finding the Number of Permutations

In how many ways can you arrange 12 books on a shelf?

 Learning Animation

ELPS Imagine that your classmate missed the lesson and does not know the terms *permutation* and *n factorial*. Help them understand and solve the Got It without using these terms. Ask: How many different ways can you arrange two books on a shelf? What do you have to multiply your answer by to find the number of ways to arrange three books? Four books? What is the pattern?

TEKS Process Standard (1)(C)

Problem 3 **Got It?** Finding a Permutation

Twelve swimmers compete in a race. In how many possible ways can the swimmers finish first, second, and third?

Learning Animation

TEKS Process Standard (1)(C)

 Problem 4 | **Got It?** | Using the Combination Formula

A service club has 8 freshmen. Five of the freshmen are to be on the clean-up crew for the town's annual picnic. How many different ways are there to choose the 5-member clean-up crew?

Learning Animation

 Problem 5 | **Got It?** | Identifying Combinations and Permutations

A yogurt shop allows you to choose any 3 of the 10 possible mix-ins for a Just Right Smoothie. How many different Just Right Smoothies are possible?

Learning Animation

 Problem 6 | **Got It?** | Finding Probabilities

Three pool balls are randomly chosen from a set numbered from 1 to 15. What is the probability of choosing first the number 1 ball, then the number 2 ball, and then the number 3 ball?

Learning Animation

Lesson 15-3 | Permutations and Combinations

Lesson Check

Do you know HOW?

1. Evaluate each expression.

   a. $3!$

   b. $_6P_2$

   c. $_6C_3$

2. How many ways can you divide a group of 12 players into 2 teams of 6?

3. At a friend's school, each student is randomly assigned a 4-digit code to access the computer network. Each digit in the code is a number from 0 to 9, and no number is repeated within a code. Is your friend likely to be assigned a code with the numbers 1, 2, 3, and 4, in any order? Calculate a probability to justify your response.

Lesson Check

Do you UNDERSTAND?

4. Vocabulary How are combinations and permutations similar? How are they different?

Math
Tools

Online
Practice

Virtual Nerd
Tutorials

5. Explain Mathematical Ideas (1)(G) Your friend says that she can calculate any probability if she knows how many successful outcomes there are. Is there something else needed? Explain.

6. Evaluate Reasonableness (1)(B) Use the combination formula to find the value of $_nC_n$ when n is a positive integer. Explain why your answer is reasonable.

TEXAS Test Practice

Gridded Response

Solve each exercise and enter your answer on the grid provided.

1. The options for a college's science classes are shown in the table.

Title	Grade Types	Times
Science 101	Pass/Fail	9:00 am
Science 105	Letter Grade	10:30 am

How many combinations of class, type, and times are available?

2. How many combinations of 4 fish can you choose from a tank containing 8 fish?

3. A bag contains 7 marbles: one each of red, orange, yellow, green, blue, violet, and white. A child randomly pulls 4 marbles from the bag. What is the probability that the marbles chosen are green, blue, red, and yellow? Round your answer to the nearest hundredth.

4. A teacher wants to choose one student to take attendance, one student to hand out papers, and one student to collect homework. If there are 16 students in the class, in how many different ways can the students be chosen?

1. 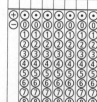 **2.** 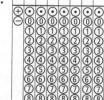 **3.** 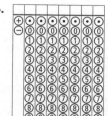 **4.**

SOLVE IT!

Suppose you are traveling from Philadelphia, PA, to San Diego, CA. Do you think the probability of rain in Philadelphia affects the probability of rain in San Diego? Justify your reasoning.

Philadelphia			San Diego	
Today	**Tomorrow**		**Today**	**Tomorrow**
Rain	Sunny		Cloudy	Partly Cloudy
43° F	**58° F**		**70° F**	**75° F**
Chance of rain: 80%	Chance of rain: 0%		Chance of rain: 50%	Chance of rain: 10%

 Apply Mathematics (1)(A) Describe another real-world situation for which you could apply the same mathematical model.

Problem 1 | **Got It?** | **Identifying Independent and Dependent Events**

Learning Animation

You roll a standard number cube. Then you flip a coin. Are the outcomes independent or dependent events? Explain.

ELPS Discuss with a classmate how your knowledge of the terms *independent* and *dependent* helps you determine the type of probability event described in the Got It.

 Problem 2 | **Got It?** | **Finding the Probability of Independent Events**

Learning Animation

You roll a standard number cube and spin the spinner at the right. What is the probability that you roll a number less than 3 and the spinner lands on a vowel?

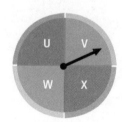

TEKS Process Standard (1)(A)

Problem 3 | **Got It?** | **Finding the Probability of Mutually Exclusive Events**

Learning Animation

Student athletes at a local high school may participate in only one sport each season. In the spring season, 15% of the athletes play baseball and 23% are on the track team. What is the probability of an athlete either playing baseball or being on the track team?

TEKS Process Standard (1)(B)

Problem 4 | **Got It?** | **Finding Probabilities of Overlapping Events**

Learning Animation

What is the probability of rolling either an odd number or a number less than 4 when rolling a standard number cube?

Lesson 15-4 | **Compound Probability**

519

Lesson Check

Do you know HOW?

1. Suppose A and B are overlapping events. What is $P(A \text{ or } B)$ if $P(A) = \frac{1}{3}$, $P(B) = 0.5$, and $P(A \text{ and } B) = 20\%$?

2. You throw two darts at the rectangular target shown below. Assuming the darts land on the target at random, what is the probability that both darts land in the shaded region?

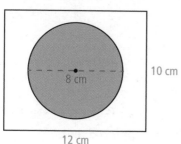

10 cm
8 cm
12 cm

3. A bag contains 3 red marbles, 5 yellow marbles, and 4 green marbles. You choose a marble at random, note the color, and then put it aside. Then you choose a second marble at random and note its color. Are you more likely to choose a red marble followed by a yellow marble, a yellow marble followed by a red marble, or are both compound events equally likely? Explain.

Math Tools

Online Practice

Virtual Nerd Tutorials

Lesson Check

Do you UNDERSTAND?

Math Tools

Online Practice

Virtual Nerd Tutorials

4. **Vocabulary** Give an example of independent events, and an example of dependent events. Describe how the examples differ.

5. **Explain Mathematical Ideas (1)(G)** Your brother says that the probability that it is cloudy tomorrow and the probability that it rains are independent events. Is your brother correct? Explain.

6. **Analyze Mathematical Relationships (1)(F)** If A and B are independent events, is it possible for $P(A$ and $B)$ to equal 1? If so, what must be true about events A and B? If not, why not?

Multiple Choice

For Exercises 1–4, choose the correct letter.

1. What is the probability of rolling a 5 on a number cube and randomly drawing the 2 of clubs from a standard deck of cards?

   A. $\frac{1}{312}$

   B. $\frac{1}{260}$

   C. $\frac{1}{24}$

   D. $\frac{1}{2}$

2. In one class, 19% of the students received an A on the last test and 13% of the students received a C. What is the probability that a randomly chosen student received an A or a C?

   F. 0.06

   G. 0.13

   H. 0.16

   J. 0.32

3. Your math team is holding a raffle as a fundraiser. Tickets are not replaced after they are drawn. Altogether, your team sold 1000 tickets. You purchased 10 tickets for yourself and sold 50 tickets to members of your family. What is the probability that the first ticket drawn is one you purchased and the second is one purchased by your family?

   A. $\frac{1}{1980}$

   B. $\frac{1}{2000}$

   C. $\frac{3}{50}$

   D. $\frac{5999}{99900}$

4. A computer randomly generates a password. The first two characters in the password are always letters. What is the probability that the first two characters of a password are a vowel followed by a consonant?

   F. $\frac{21}{130}$

   G. $\frac{1}{25}$

   H. $\frac{105}{676}$

   J. $\frac{26}{26}$

Short Response

5. The results of a survey revealed that 26% of the students read fiction in their spare time, 21% of the students read non-fiction, and 7% don't read in their spare time. What is the probability that a randomly chosen student reads fiction or doesn't read in her spare time?

Lesson 15-4 | Compound Probability

522

SOLVE IT!

The table below shows the number of students who passed their driving test as well as whether they took a driver's education class to prepare. What effect, if any, does taking the driver's education class have?

Interactive
Exploration

Vocabulary
Online

	Passed	Failed	Totals
Took the class	32	7	39
Did not take the class	18	23	41
Totals	50	30	80

⭐ **Apply Mathematics (1)(A)** Describe another real-world situation for which you could apply the same mathematical model.

Problem 1 | **Got It?** | Using a Two-Way Frequency Table

The two-way frequency table shows the number of male and female students by grade level on the prom committee. What is the probability that a member of the prom committee is a male who is a junior?

Learning Animation

	Male	Female	Totals
Juniors	3	4	7
Seniors	3	2	5
Totals	6	6	12

ELPS Discuss the answers to the following questions with a classmate. How many junior males are on the committee? How many students are on the committee in all? If you pick a student from the committee at random, what is the probability that the student will be a male who is a junior? Give your answer as a fraction, a decimal, and a percent.

Lesson 15-5 | Conditional Probability With Frequency Tables

Problem 2 | **Got It?** | **Finding Probability**

a. What is the probability that a randomly selected person is 30–45 years old, given that the person is in favor of the minimum-wage bill?

Age Group	For	Against	No Opinion	Totals
18–29	310	50	20	380
30–45	200	30	10	240
46–60	120	20	30	170
Over 60	150	20	40	210
Totals	780	120	100	1000

 Learning Animation

b. What is the probability that a randomly selected person is not 18–29, given that the person is in favor of the minimum-wage bill?

TEKS Process Standard (1)(F)

 Problem 3 | **Got It?** | **Using Relative Frequencies**

A company has 150 sales representatives. What is the probability that a randomly selected sales representative, who did not attend the seminar, did not see an increase in sales?

 Learning Animation

	Attended Seminar	Did Not Attend Seminar	Totals
Increased Sales	0.48	0.02	0.5
No Increase in Sales	0.32	0.18	0.5
Totals	0.8	0.2	1

Lesson Check

Do you know HOW?

1. Use the two-way frequency table to find *P*(democrat and supports the issue) and *P*(democrat | supports the issue).

	Supports the Issue	Does Not Support the Issue	Totals
Democrat	24	36	60
Republican	27	33	60
Totals	51	69	120

2. According to the survey results in the two-way frequency table, is a student more likely to play an instrument, given that he or she is a junior; or to be a junior, given that he or she plays an instrument? Explain.

	Plays Instrument	Does Not Play Instrument	Totals
Junior	0.15	0.45	0.6
Senior	0.2	0.2	0.4
Totals	0.35	0.65	1

3. The probability that a student attended the school play, given that the student is female, is 0.4. Use this information to complete the two-way frequency table.

	Attended School Play	Did Not Attend Play	Totals
Male	16	14	30
Female			20
Totals			50

Lesson 15-5 | Conditional Probability With Frequency Tables

Lesson Check

Do you UNDERSTAND?

Math Tools

Online Practice

Virtual Nerd Tutorials

4. **Vocabulary** What is a two-way frequency table?

5. **Explain Mathematical Ideas (1)(G)** Using the table from Exercise 1, a student calculated the relative frequency of those who do not support the issue, given that they are Republican, as $\frac{33}{33 + 36} \approx 0.478$. Is this correct? If not, explain the error.

6. **Use Representations to Communicate Mathematical Ideas (1)(E)** Suppose A means that a student is female and B means that a student plays sports. What does $P(B \mid A)$ represent?

TEXAS Test Practice

Multiple Choice

For Exercises 1–4, choose the correct letter.

The table below shows the number of participants at a charity event who walked or ran, and who wore a red t-shirt or a blue t-shirt. Use the table for Exercises 1–4.

	Blue t-shirt	Red t-shirt	Totals
Walk	80	30	110
Run	20	30	50
Totals	100	60	160

1. What is the probability that a randomly chosen person ran and wore a blue t-shirt?

A. 0.125   **B.** 0.25   **C.** 0.4   **D.** 25

2. Which of the following is a true statement?

F. The relative frequency of participants who walked and wore blue t-shirts is 0.8.

G. P(walked | wore a red t-shirt) and P(ran | wore a red t-shirt) are equal.

H. The probability that a randomly chosen person ran or wore a red t-shirt is greater than the probability that a randomly chosen person wore a blue t-shirt.

J. The probability that a randomly chosen person walked and wore a red t-shirt is 0.5.

3. What is P(ran | wore a blue t-shirt)?

A. 0.2   **B.** 0.25   **C.** 0.4   **D.** 0.8

4. A door prize was given to a randomly chosen participant. What is the probability that the winner wore a red t-shirt?

F. 0.375   **G.** 0.4   **H.** 0.5   **J.** 0.6

Short Response

5. When calculating $P(B \mid A)$, what does A represent?

SOLVE IT!

Suppose the probability of rain on Saturday is 40%. What is the probability that you clean the garage on Saturday?

Interactive Exploration

Vocabulary Online

Use Representations to Communicate Mathematical Ideas (1)(E) Describe how the representation you used to solve the problem successfully organizes and communicates your ideas.

Problem 1 | **Got It?** | Using Conditional Probabilities

Learning
Animation

In the study in Problem 1, half of the volunteers received the drug, and the other half received a placebo. The probability of a volunteer receiving the placebo and having his or her health improve was 20%. What is the conditional probability of a volunteer's health improving, given that he or she received the placebo?

 Problem 2 | **Got It?** | Comparing Conditional Probabilities

Learning
Animation

The survey in Problem 2 showed that 45% of pet owners own a dog, 27% own a cat, and 5% own a dog, a cat, and at least one other type of pet.

a. What is the conditional probability that a pet owner owns a cat and some other type of pet, given that they own a dog?

b. What is the conditional probability that a pet owner owns a dog and some other type of pet, given that they own a cat?

c. Can you calculate the conditional probability of owning another pet for a pet owner owning a cat and no dogs? Explain.

Problem 3 | **Got It?** | Selecting With Replacement

Learning
Animation

Refer to the picture in Problem 3. What is the probability that you randomly choose a bird and then, after replacing the first tile, a flower?

Problem 4 | Got It? | Selecting Without Replacement

Refer to the picture in Problem 3. What is the probability that you will randomly choose a flower and then, without replacing the first tile, a bird?

Learning Animation

TEKS Process Standard (1)(E)

 Problem 5 | Got It? | Using a Tree Diagram

a. A soccer team wins 65% of its games on muddy fields and 30% of their games on dry fields. The probability of the field being muddy for their next game is 70%. What is the probability that the team will win their next game?

Learning Animation

b. If the probability of the field being muddy increases, how will that influence the probability of the soccer team winning their next game? Explain.

ELPS Discuss with a classmate how using tree diagrams can help you solve probability problems. Answer questions such as: What situations can be solved using a tree diagram? How are calculations made after the information is organized? As you speak, ask your partner to assist you when you are uncertain how to express your idea or have difficulty pronouncing words.

Lesson Check

Do you know HOW?

1. A jar contains 10 large red marbles, 4 small red marbles, 6 large blue marbles, and 5 small blue marbles. Which of the conditional probabilities is greater, $P(\text{red} \mid \text{small})$ or $P(\text{small} \mid \text{red})$? Explain.

Math
Tools

Online
Practice

Virtual Nerd
Tutorials

2. In a survey of visitors to a museum, 60% of the people surveyed were male. The probability that a visitor was a male and shopped at the gift shop was 40%. What is the probability that a visitor did not shop at the gift shop, given that the visitor was male?

3. A teacher assigned a term paper to all of the students in three class periods. There are an equal number of students in each class. Out of all the students, $\frac{1}{6}$ were in Period 1 and got an A on the paper, $\frac{1}{9}$ were in Period 2 and got an A, and $\frac{1}{8}$ were in Period 3 and got an A. What is the probability that a student got an A on the paper, given that he or she was in Period 1 or 2?

Lesson Check

Do you UNDERSTAND?

4. **Vocabulary** How is finding a conditional probability like finding a compound probability? How are they different?

Math Tools

Online Practice

Virtual Nerd Tutorials

5. **Explain Mathematical Ideas (1)(G)** Your friend says that the conditional probability of one event is 0% if it is independent of another given event. Do you agree? Explain.

6. **Analyze Mathematical Relationships (1)(F)** What must be true about a situation in which the probability of event B, given that event A has occurred, is equal to the probability of events A and B occurring? Explain.

Multiple Choice

For Exercises 1–4, choose the correct letter.

For Exercises 1 and 2, use the following information.

A physician determined that on average, 40% of his patients get the flu each year. Of this group, 10% received the flu vaccine. Of the patients who do not get the flu, 20% received the flu vaccine.

1. What is the probability that a patient did not receive the flu vaccine?

A. 0.36   **C.** 0.84

B. 0.48   **D.** 0.90

2. What is the probability that a patient received the vaccine and got the flu?

F. 0.04   **H.** 0.25

G. 0.10   **J.** 0.40

3. Of the 85% of the students in a class who studied for a test, 75% passed the test. Of the 15% of the students who did not study, 30% passed. What is the combined probability of passing?

A. 0.3   **C.** 0.6825

B. 0.6375   **D.** 0.75

4. In a survey, 60% of the people own a laptop computer, 80% own a desktop computer, and 30% own both. What is the probability that a person owns a desktop, given that he or she owns a laptop?

F. 0.3   **H.** 0.5

G. 0.4   **J.** 0.6

Short Response

5. How can you derive a formula for $P(A \text{ and } B)$ from the formula for $P(B \mid A)$?